ONE BRIGHT SUMME...
successful playwright V...
becomes suddenly and br...
Vietnamese servant, and ...
ranch-house to work on a...
bright summer morning, ...
– and his shot guns – vanished, the telephone dead, the plugs
torn from his car.
. . . This is the chilling opening of maestro James Hadley
Chase's new thriller!

JAMES HADLEY CHASE

One Bright Summer
Morning

GRAFTON BOOKS

A Division of the Collins Publishing Group

LONDON GLASGOW
TORONTO SYDNEY AUCKLAND

Grafton Books
A Division of the Collins Publishing Group
8 Grafton Street, London W1X 3LA

Published by Grafton Books 1965
Reprinted 1967, 1968, 1969, 1973, 1977, 1978
1980, 1981, 1984, 1986

First published in Great Britain by
Robert Hale Ltd 1963

ISBN 0-586-02544-8

Printed and bound in Great Britain by
Collins, Glasgow

Set in Monotype Baskerville

One Bright Summer Morning

CHAPTER ONE

AT five-thirty-seven on what promised to be a bright summer morning, Victor Dermott came awake suddenly in a cold sweat of fear.

Victor Dermott was thirty-eight years of age. He was powerfully built, tall and dark. From time to time, he had been mistaken for Gregory Peck by short-sighted autograph hunters. This was something he shrugged off, but which had secretly annoyed him. It had annoyed him because he was successful and wealthy in his own right. During the past ten years he had written four very successful plays that had been produced on Broadway, and were even now earning him a substantial income in the capital cities of Europe. His success and wealth hadn't spoilt him. He was considered by those who came into contact with him as a nice guy: that was what he was. He was happily married to a twenty-eight-year-old redhead who adored him as much as he adored her. They had a ten-month-old baby.

Two months previous to this hot summer morning, Vic Dermott had suddenly conceived an idea for his next play. It was one of those white-hot inspirations that demanded to be written at once and without interruption, without the clamour of the telephone bell and without any social commitments.

Dermott had asked his secretary, a grey-haired and efficient woman named Vera Synder, to find him a place where he could work for three months in complete isolation. Within two days, she had found him the exact place: a compact, *de luxe* ranch house on the fringe of the Nevada desert, some fifty miles from Pitt City and some twenty miles from Boston Creek.

Pitt City was a major town, but Boston Creek had little to offer except a service station, a number of cafés and a general store.

The ranch house was called "Wastelands". It was owned by an elderly couple who spent most of their lives travelling in Europe. They were happy to rent the place to such a well-known person as Victor Dermott.

The ranch house had a long private drive that met a dirt road that in its turn went on a further fifteen miles through scrub and sand to meet the main highway to Pitt City. For genuine isolation and de luxe comfort, it would be hard to find a better place to live in than Wastelands.

Vic Dermott had driven with his wife, Carrie, to inspect the ranch house. He saw at once that it was exactly what he wanted and he signed a three-month agreement without a quibble.

Wastelands had a big living-room, a dining-room, a study-cum-gun-room, three bedrooms, three bathrooms, a well-equipped kitchen and a swimming pool. It also had a garage for four cars, a tennis court and a go-kart track complete with four go-karts. Some two hundred yards from the house was a five-roomed wooden cabin for the staff.

The rent came a little high, but as Vic was making plenty of money, and the place pleased him, he didn't argue about the cost.

But before deciding to take the ranch house, he had talked it over with Carrie.

"It could be pretty dull for you," he had pointed out. "We won't see anyone until the play is finished. Perhaps it would be better if you stayed home and I went there on my own."

This Carrie wouldn't consider. She would have plenty to do, she said. She had Junior to look after. She would do Vic's typing. She would do the cooking, and she would take along a couple of unfinished paintings she had been working on.

They decided to take with them only one servant: a young Vietnamese, Di-Long, who had been with them for just over a year. He was not only highly domesticated, but also a trained mechanic. Being so far from a service station, Dermott had decided he should have someone around who could cope with a car breakdown.

After two months of hard, concentrated work, the play

was practically finished. Vic was now polishing the dialogue and wrestling with the second act curtain that didn't entirely satisfy him. He was sure that in another couple of weeks the play would be ready for production and he was certain he had written yet another big success.

During the two months they had spent at Wastelands, both Vic and Carrie had come to love the place. They regretted that in a few more weeks they would have to return to the hustle and bustle of their Los Angeles home. For the first time, since their honeymoon, they had been given the opportunity of being entirely alone together and they liked the experience. They now realized the pressure of their social life, the continuous parties, the constant ringing of the telephone bell had been robbing them of the experience of getting to know each other more intimately and also had been robbing them of having the time to watch their baby growing up.

Although Wastelands was a big success with the Dermotts, it was far from being a success with their Vietnamese servant who became more and more morose as the weeks went by and more indifferent in his work.

Both Vic and Carrie worried about this little man. They wished he had a wife to console him. They encouraged him to take the second car into Pitt City to see a movie, but they understood when he shrugged irritably that a movie had to be pretty good to make a fifty-mile journey there and back in a day.

Every so often Vic would lose patience, pointing out to Carrie that Di-Long was being paid three times the amount anyone in their right minds would pay a servant. Carrie, who had a prickly conscience regarding servants, had argued that Di-Long, no matter how much he was paid, had reason to complain about his loneliness.

This story begins on a July morning, a little after five-thirty, when Vic Dermott came awake with a start to find his body clammy with cold sweat and his heart thumping so violently he had difficulty in breathing.

He lay motionless: all his senses alert. He could hear the ticking of the bedside clock and the faint rumble of the refrigerator in the kitchen as it turned itself on, but the rest of the ranch house was silent.

He couldn't remember having had a bad dream to frighten him, and yet, here he was, woken from a deep sleep and more frightened than he had ever been before in his life.

He raised his head and looked over at the twin bed in which Carrie was sleeping peacefully. He regarded her for a brief moment, then he looked across the room to where Junior was also sleeping peacefully.

He took his handkerchief from under his pillow and wiped his sweating face. The silence, the familiar room and the fact that his two most precious possessions were undisturbed lessened this odd fear that gripped him, and after a few seconds, his heartbeats gradually returned to normal.

I must have been dreaming, he thought, but it's odd I can't remember . . .

Not satisfied, he threw off the sheet and slid out of bed.

Moving silently so as not to wake Carrie, he put on his dressing-gown and thrust his feet into heel-less slippers. Then he crossed the room, gently opened the bedroom door and moved out into the big square-shaped lobby.

Although his heartbeat was now normal, he still had a feeling of acute uneasiness that worried him. Quietly, he went into the big lounge and looked around. Everything was just as he had left it the previous night. He crossed the room and looked through the big window across the patio at the fountain throwing its lively cascade of water, at the lounging chairs and at the magazine Carrie had left lying on the paved terrace.

He walked into his work-room and looked around. He looked out of the window at the staff cabin some two hundred yards across the way where Di-Long slept. There was no sign of life, but that didn't surprise him as Di-Long never got up before half past seven.

Unable to find an explanation for his uneasiness, he shrugged irritably and made his way to the kitchen. He knew he wouldn't be able to sleep if he returned to his bed.

He might as well make some coffee, he told himself, and begin work.

He entered the kitchen, unlocked and opened the door that led onto another small patio with a gate that the Dermotts always kept open so that Bruno, their Alsatian dog, could have the run of the place, and yet sleep in his kennel during the night.

Vic whistled for the dog and then plugged in the coffee percolator. He put the bowl containing Bruno's breakfast on the floor by the door, then he crossed the lobby into the bathroom.

Ten minutes later, shaved, showered and dressed in a white singlet, blue cotton trousers and white sneakers, he made his way back to the kitchen. He was about to turn off the percolator when he paused and frowned.

Bruno's breakfast was untouched. There was no sign of the dog.

As he stared at the untouched food in the bowl, Vic again had the prickly feeling of fear crawl up his spine. This was something that hadn't happened before since the Dermotts had moved into the ranch house. A single sharp whistle had always brought Bruno bounding into the kitchen.

Vic walked quickly across the patio and peered into the kennel. It was empty. He whistled again and stood for some moments waiting and listening, then he went to the gate and looked out into the scrub land and the sand, but there was no sign of the dog.

It was early, he told himself. He usually got up around seven. The dog was probably chasing a marmot, but it was unusual . . . it was becoming a tiresomely unusual morning.

He returned to the kitchen, poured coffee, added cream and took the cup into his work-room. He sat at his desk and sipped a little of the coffee before lighting a cigarette.

He picked up the nearly completed manuscript and began to read the last few pages. He turned a page, then realized he hadn't registered what he had just read. Impatiently, he turned back the page and began to read again, but his mind was now fully occupied with Bruno. Where was the dog?

He pushed aside the manuscript, finished his coffee and went back to the kitchen.

Bruno's breakfast remained untouched.

Again Vic crossed the patio to the gate. Again he whistled and looked across the white sand dunes.

He had a sudden feeling of loneliness and he had an urge to talk to Carrie, but after hesitating, he decided not to disturb her. He returned to his work-room and sat down in the lounging chair and tried to relax.

From where he sat, he could see through the big window the sun rising behind the dunes. He watched the red ball appear, its light colouring the vast sweep of the desert to rose pink. Usually this sight fascinated him, but this morning he was only aware of the vastness of the space surrounding the ranch house, and for the first time since he had come to Wastelands, he was uncomfortably aware of their isolation.

The sudden whimpering cry of his son brought him to his feet. He went quickly across the lobby and into the bedroom.

Junior was beginning his morning bawl for his breakfast. Carrie was already sitting up in the bed, stretching. She smiled at him as he paused in the doorway.

"You're early. What's the time?" she asked and yawned.

"Half past six," Vic said and went over to the cot. He lifted Junior who immediately stopped crying at the familiar firm touch of his father and he gave Vic a toothless grin.

"Couldn't you sleep?" Carrie asked as she slid out of bed.

"I was restless."

Vic sat on the end of the bed and held Junior. He watched his wife walk across the bedroom and into the bathroom. He felt a little surge of pleasure at the sight of her in her transparent nightdress that revealed her exciting young body and her long, lovely legs.

Fifteen minutes later, Carrie was feeding Junior while Vic lolled on the bed and watched. This was a moment that always gave him considerable pleasure.

Carrie said abruptly, "Did you hear that motor-cycle last night?"

Watching this ritual of feeding, Vic had forgotten his fears, but these words from Carrie brought him abruptly alert.

"Motor-cycle? I heard nothing . . . last night?"

"Someone came out here on a motor-cycle," Carrie said. She put Junior back in his cot. "It was around two o'clock. I didn't hear the cycle go away."

Vic ran his fingers through his hair.

"What does that mean, honey?"

Carrie came away from the cot and sat on the bed.

"I didn't hear the motor-cycle drive away," she repeated. "I heard it arrive. The engine stopped . . . then nothing."

"It was probably the Highway Patrol," Vic said and reached in his pocket for a pack of cigarettes. "He comes out here from time to time . . . remember?"

"But he didn't go away," Carrie said.

"Of course he went away. What happened was you went off to sleep. You didn't hear him go. If he hadn't gone away, he'd be here now, wouldn't he? He isn't."

Carrie stared at him.

"But how do you know he isn't still here?"

Vic moved impatiently.

"Look, darling . . . why should he be? Anyway, Bruno would have started barking . . ." Vic paused and frowned. "Come to think of it . . . Bruno hasn't shown up this morning. I whistled, but he didn't come. It's damned odd." He got to his feet and went quickly into the kitchen. The bowl of food remained untouched. He went to the door and whistled again.

Joining him, Carrie said, "Where can he be?"

"Chasing something, I guess. I'll go and look for him."

Junior, feeling neglected, began to bawl and Carrie hurried back to the bedroom. Vic hesitated, then he set off on the long walk down to the entrance gate. He passed the shut-up staff cabin. The time now was seven o'clock. Di-Long still had half an hour before he showed himself. As Vic walked down the long drive, he paused from time to time to give his long, piercing whistle.

He finally reached the five-barred gate and he looked up

and down the narrow dirt road beyond without seeing a movement of anything alive.

Then he looked down at the sandy road. Between the tyre tracks of his car, he saw the unmistakable imprint of two single tyre tracks . . . the tracks of a motor-cycle. These tracks led from afar, direct to his gate and they stopped there. He looked to his left, but the tracks were no longer visible. It seemed, on the face of it, that someone had driven from Pitt City highway, up the dirt road to his gate. The driver and his machine had then vanished into space. There was no sign that the motor-cycle had come up the drive nor had gone on to Boston Creek. The machine had stopped at the gate and then had apparently dissolved into nothingness.

For several minutes, Vic stared at the motor-cycle tracks, and up and down the dirt road, then turning, he stared up the drive. The strange, uneasy feeling of loneliness closed over him again and he started back towards the ranch house at a pace that set him sweating in the growing heat of the early sun.

As he passed the staff cabin, he came into sight of the ranch house. Carrie was standing in the open doorway and she was waving to him. Her movements were quick and urgent. As he approached her, he called, "What is it?"

"Vic! The guns have gone."

He now reached her. He could see she was frightened. Her blue eyes were round and alarmed.

"Guns? Gone?"

"I went into your room . . . the guns aren't in the rack!"

He went quickly into the gun-room. The gun rack was out of sight of his desk, around the L-shaped room. He paused and stared at the empty rack. There had been four shotguns: a .45 and two .22 rifles in the rack. The rack now stood empty.

Vic stared at the empty rack, feeling the hairs on the nape of his neck bristle. He turned to find Carrie watching him.

"They were here last night," she said in a small, frightened voice.

"That's right." Vic walked over to his desk and pulled

open the bottom drawer. In this drawer he kept a .38 Police Special automatic presented to him by the Los Angeles Chief of Police.

It came as a sickening shock when he looked into the empty drawer with its slight smear of oil where the gun had been.

"Your gun too?" Carrie asked, moving forward.

He forced the feeling of panic that gripped him into control and turning, he smiled at her: a forced smile, but a smile.

"Looks like someone broke in here last night and grabbed all the guns," he said. "I guess I'd better call the police."

"That motor-cycle I heard . . ."

"Could be. I'll call the police."

As he picked up the telephone receiver, Carrie said, a rise in her voice, "He – he could still be here. I told you . . . I didn't hear him leave."

Vic scarcely heard what she was saying for he was realizing as he held the telephone receiver to his ear and as he began to dial that the telephone was dead.

Speaking as calmly as he could, Vic said, "Seems the telephone is on the blink." Slowly he replaced the receiver.

Carrie said breathlessly, "It was all right last night. We had that call from . . ."

"I know," Vic cut in. "Well, it's not working now."

They faced each other.

"What's happened to Bruno?" Carrie asked. She folded her arms across her breasts, her blue eyes growing rounder. "Do you think . . . ?"

"Now don't get worked up," Vic said sharply. "Someone broke in here last night, disconnected the telephone and took the guns. It's possible he has put Bruno out of action."

Carrie flinched.

"You mean . . . Bruno's dead?"

"I don't know, darling. Drugged perhaps . . . I don't know."

Carrie came into the room and moved quickly to Vic, putting her arms around him. He held her, feeling her slight body trembling. "Oh, Vic, I'm frightened! What is it? What are we going to do?"

He patted her, holding her close to him, aware that he too was a little frightened: aware too of the loneliness of the place. He thought of Di-Long.

"Look, you go back to Junior. I'm going to wake Di-Long. I'll get him to stay with you while I take a look around. Come on, Carrie, you don't have to look so scared."

With his arm around her, he walked with her into the bedroom where Junior, in his cot, was kicking his fat legs and making his usual routine noises.

"You stay right here. I won't be a couple of minutes."

"No!" Carrie gripped his arm. "Don't leave me, Vic! You mustn't leave me!"

"But, darling . . ."

"Please! Don't leave me!"

He hesitated, then nodded.

"Okay, okay, now don't get worked up."

He went over to the open window that looked out onto the staff cabin, some two hundred yards away.

Leaning out, he shouted, "Di-Long! Hey! Di-Long!"

Only silence greeted his shout. The small cabin with its tightly closed green shutters showed no sign of life.

"Di-Long!!"

Carrie was slipping into a pair of slacks and a lightweight sweater. Her movements were hurried and clumsy.

He turned away from the window.

"That guy sleeps like the dead," he said. "Come on, Carrie. Let's go over and wake him. Bring Junior."

With Carrie carrying the baby, they walked along the path between the two squares of lawn, kept green by concealed sprinklers, over to the staff cabin.

Vic knocked on the door. They waited, feeling the sun now hot on their backs. Junior, blinking in the sunshine, doubled his fat hand into a fist and attempted to push it into Carrie's eye, but she was used to this move and avoided the probing fist by a quick jerk of her head.

"I'm going in," Vic said impatiently. "You wait here."

He turned the door handle and the door yielded. He walked into the sitting-room.

"Di-Long!"

There was no movement. A tap dripped steadily in the kitchen. There was no other sound.

Vic hesitated, then he crossed the room and pushed open the door that led into the bedroom which gave off a faint acrid smell and was in darkness. He groped for the light switch, found it and turned it down.

The small, neat room was empty. The single bed, against the far wall had been slept in. Vic could see the impression of Di-Long's head on the pillow. The single sheet had been thrown aside: the bottom sheet was slightly crumpled.

He paused only long enough to satisfy himself that Di-Long wasn't there, then he went into the kitchen. After a quick look round, he joined Carrie.

"He's gone!"

Carrie visibly relaxed.

"You mean he stole the guns . . . and Bruno? Do you think that's what happened?" she asked, holding Junior close to her.

"Could be." Vic was puzzled, but now he also was relaxing. This seemed to be the solution to the mystery. "He wasn't happy here. He adored Bruno. Yes . . . I guess that's what he did. He probably got a pal of his to fetch him on the motor-cycle."

"But the guns?"

"Yeah." Vic ran his fingers through his hair and he frowned. After a moment's thought, he went on, "You never know with these Vietnamese. He may belong to some secret society who need guns. Looks as if he put the phone out of order to get a clear start."

"But how could he have taken all those guns on a motor-cycle . . . and Bruno?" Carrie asked.

"Maybe he's taken one of the cars. I'll go and see. Look, we'll drive down to Pitt City. We'll get the police up here. This is a job for them to handle."

Carrie nodded. Vic was relieved to see she no longer looked frightened.

"I'll get things ready for Junior. You get the car."

Vic watched her walk quickly to the ranch house. He started towards the garage, then paused. A thought struck him. He went back to Di-Long's bedroom. The closet in which Di-Long kept his clothes and his possessions stood against the wall to the left of the bed. Vic opened the doors. He looked at the three neat suits and the white uniforms that Di-Long kept immaculate. On one of the shelves was the electric razor that Vic had given Di-Long last Christmas. By its side was a Kodak camera Vic had also given him when Vic had changed to a Leica: two of Di-Long's most treasured possessions.

Vic stood staring at these two articles, feeling his heart beginning to thump. Di-Long would never have left these behind unless something extraordinary had happened to have forced him to do so . . . but what could have happened?

Turning quickly, he walked with long strides to the garage and swung up the big door. The blue and white Cadillac and the Mercury estate wagon stood side by side. It was a relief to see them. He got into the Cadillac. The key was in the ignition lock and he turned it, then put his foot down on the gas pedal to start the engine. There was a whirring noise, but the engine didn't fire. He tried three times to start the car, but the engine refused to fire. He got out of the car and crossed over to the estate wagon and attempted to start that. Again he was greeted with the whirring noise, and again this engine refused to start.

He got out of the estate wagon and wiped his sweating hands on the seat of his cotton pants. Then he opened the hood of the Cadillac. He had little knowledge of cars, but he saw at a glance that all the sparking plugs had been removed. A quick look at the estate wagon told the same story.

Someone had removed the plugs from both cars and they were now immobile.

Vic stood motionless in the big garage between the two useless cars. He felt a drop of cold sweat run down his face and he wiped it away with the back of his hand. If he had

been alone, this situation would have been a challenge to
him, but he kept thinking of Carrie and the baby and he
felt frightened. What was going on? he asked himself. No
Bruno, no Di-Long, no guns, no telephone and now no cars.

He suddenly remembered that Carrie was alone with
Junior in the ranch house. He left the garage and with long
strides he ran across the lawn.

He found Carrie in the bedroom, packing a small suitcase with baby things. She turned as he came into the
bedroom and he paused. They looked at each other. He saw
her stiffen. Her hand went to her mouth. He realized he
must be looking pretty scared and he tried to control himself without much success.

"What is it?" Carrie asked sharply.

"This could be trouble," he said. "The cars have been
put out of action. We are marooned here. I don't know
what it all means."

Carrie sat abruptly on the bed as if she no longer had any
strength in her legs.

"What's happened to the cars?"

"Someone's taken the plugs. Di-Long left his camera and
razor. I'm willing to bet he wouldn't have left them unless . . ." Vic stopped, frowning, then he sat on the bed
beside Carrie. "I don't want to frighten you, but this could
be serious. I don't know what it's all about, but someone
has been here . . . someone who . . ." He stopped short,
realizing he was talking too much.

Carrie stared at him, her face pale.

"Then you don't think Di-Long stole the guns?"

"Not now. He would never have left his camera or his
razor if he had walked out on us. I just don't know what to
think."

"Then what's happened to him? What's happened to
Bruno?"

"I don't know."

Carrie got abruptly to her feet.

"Let's get out of here, Vic!" Her voice was a little shrill.
"Now! I'm not staying here!"

"We can't get out of here!" Vic said. "It's fifteen miles

to the highway. The sun's getting hot. We can't walk all that way with Junior."

"I'm not staying here! We'll walk! Anything but staying here! You carry Junior. I'll bring his things. I'm not staying here a moment longer!"

Vic stood up, hesitated, then shrugged.

"It'll be a hell of a walk. Well, all right. Let's walk then. We should have something to drink. I'll fill a vacuum flask. In another hour the sun will be fierce."

"I don't care . . . hurry, Vic!"

He went into the kitchen and filled a flask with ice-cold Coke. He put two packs of cigarettes in his shirt pockets. He went into his work-room and took his cheque book and three one-hundred dollar bills he always kept by him for an emergency. These he stuffed into his hip pocket, then he returned to the bedroom.

"You'd better wear your sun hat. I'll use an umbrella to shade Junior," he said. "Take your jewels, Carrie. We'll . . ."

He broke off as Carrie gave a sudden suppressed scream. She was looking at his feet, all colour drained from her face.

Vic followed her staring gaze down to his white sneakers. The right shoe, along the inner edge, was stained red . . . the red was unmistakable.

Somewhere during his walk around the estate he had stepped into a puddle of blood.

CHAPTER TWO

To understand what had been happening at Wastelands, it is necessary to go back three months to the day on which Solly Lucas, a Los Angeles attorney, put an automatic pistol to his mouth and blew off the top of his balding head.

Although, as a gangster's mouthpiece, Solly Lucas had a disreputable reputation, he was considered generally as a very smart cookie with a golden touch for the Stock Market. He was sixty-five years of age when he finished his life. For the past thirty years he had been the mouthpiece and investment fixer for one of the most notorious criminals since Al Capone: a man known as Big Jim Kramer.

Kramer, now close on sixty years of age, had begun his criminal career as bodyguard to Roger Touhy. He had risen slowly and murderously to a gang boss, had been elected a member of Murder Incorporated and had eventually become the iron hand that ruled the Bakery and the Milk Unions: a man who finally amassed a fortune of six million dollars from the rackets and had been smart enough to have paid some of his income tax.

Although the Federal Bureau of Investigation had known that Kramer was a major criminal, a vice-king and the brains behind some of the biggest bank robberies, they had never been able to pin a charge on him. The combination of Kramer's guile and Lucas's brilliant legal smoke screens had proved too much for them.

When he had reached his fifty-fifth birthday, Kramer decided to pull out of the rackets. It is never easy for a gang boss to quit the rackets. Usually, the moment he appears to be chickening out, some hood arrives with a gun, and that is the end of the gang boss, but Kramer was no fool. He knew this. He had six million dollars salted away. He parted with two million to buy himself security and future peace. These two million dollars so greased his exit that he was one of the very few important gang bosses who was able to quit the rackets and retire in comfort, security and obscurity.

With four million dollars and Lucas as his investment manager, Kramer had no fears for the future. He bought himself a luxury villa at Paradise City, not far from Los Angeles and settled down to enjoy the social life of retirement.

While he had been a gang boss he had married a night-club singer, Helene Dors, a slim, big-eyed blonde, older than she looked, who accepted Kramer for what he was, not because of his money nor for his power but because she was unfortunate enough to fall in love with him.

But once away from his criminal activities and his associates, Kramer became a surprisingly genial man who played an excellent game of golf, a sound game of bridge, who could drink without making a nuisance of himself and who was accepted by Paradise City's society – who had no idea of his past activities – as a well-off, retired business man and was generally popular. Paradise City's society also took to Helene who, although a little over-weight now and slightly faded, had still a gay, lyrical voice and could sit at a piano and improvize songs a little *risqué*, but never vulgar and caused fun on those evenings when the Country Club could get dull.

There were times when Kramer was on his own, when Helene had gone to Los Angeles for a day's shopping, when rain cancelled a golf date, that he would hanker for the excitement of being a gang boss again. Although he hankered for his lost power, he did nothing about it. He was in the clear and that was something that seldom happened to a man with his criminal past. The F.B.I. had never caught up with him. Solly was turning his money over at an excellent yearly profit. He was, he kept reminding himself, well out of the rackets and a lucky guy.

In spite of his determination to keep out of the rackets, Kramer spent some of his spare time planning a spectacular robbery, a kidnapping or a bank raid. These plans, blue-printed to the final details, helped to pass the time and were to him like chess problems. He would select the Chase

National Bank in Los Angeles and conceive a plan where five men could walk into the bank and walk out again with a million dollars. On a wet afternoon while Helene was working on her *petit-point* he would work out a blueprint for the kidnapping of the daughter of a Texas billionaire with a ransom of several million dollars. These exercises in crime not only amused him, but kept his mind alert. He had no intention of putting them into practice. Never once did he confide in Helene what he was thinking about in those long hours when he sat silent, staring into the flickering fire. Had she known what was sometimes going through his mind, she would have been horrified.

On the morning that Solly Lucas shot himself, Kramer had had one of his best rounds of golf. He and his partner entered the club bar, and they ordered double gins with a lime chaser.

It was while Kramer was setting down his glass after a thirsty drink that the barman said, "There's a call for you, Mr. Kramer, from L.A."

Kramer got to his feet, went over to the booth and shut himself in. He lifted the receiver, humming happily under his breath. The humming quickly ceased. The harsh, unsteady voice of Abe Jacobs, Solly Lucas's chief clerk, told him the news.

"Shot himself?" Kramer repeated and he suddenly felt a vacuum forming inside him.

He had known Solly for thirty years. He had known him to be a brilliant if crooked attorney with an uncanny instinct for making money, but he had also known him to be a fool regarding women, and an extravagant and reckless gambler. Lucas wouldn't have killed himself unless he had come to the end of his financial road. Kramer felt cold sweat break out on his forehead. He had a sudden sickening fear for his four million dollars.

It took two weeks of concentrated ferreting to discover just why Solly had ended his life. It seemed that he had four important clients . . . Kramer being one of them. Each of these clients had trusted him with large sums of money. Lucas had used this money for his own purposes. He had been unlucky, or perhaps it was he was getting too old for a speculative gamble. He had thrown in more and more of his clients' money to hold off disaster. Land, building and Stock speculations had finally sunk him into a bottomless pit. When the crash came he was in the hole for nine million dollars, including Kramer's four million. Lucas knew Kramer. This was something Kramer would never forgive. He saved Kramer the trouble of killing him; he killed himself.

It took Kramer some time to accept the fact that Lucas, who had been his prop and his friend for the past thirty years, had betrayed him into poverty. Apart from five thousand dollars in his bank, his shares, his bonds and even the cash in his safe deposit had vanished with Lucas's death.

He sat in Lucas's big, luxury office, facing Abe Jacobs, a tall, thin man with an egg-shaped head and close-set, shifty eyes.

Jacobs said quietly, "There it is, Mr. Kramer. I'm sorry. I had no idea what he was doing. He never confided in me. You're not the only one. He's lost something close on nine million dollars in two years. I guess he must have been crazy."

Kramer got slowly to his feet. For the first time in his life, he felt old.

"Keep me out of this Abe," he said. "I haven't lost a dime . . . hear me? If the Press get on to me, I'll get on to you!"

He went out into the sunlit street and got into his car. He sat for some minutes, staring blankly through the windscreen, seeing nothing but his bleak, dollarless future. Should he tell Helene? He decided he wouldn't tell her, anyway for the time being. But what was he going to do? How was he now going to live? He thought of the new Cadillac he had ordered. There was this mink stole he had promised Helene for her birthday. He had booked a suite on a luxury liner for a trip to the Far East: not paid for yet, but Helene was wildly excited and could talk of little else. He had several commitments that involved a large sum of money. The paltry five thousand dollars in his bank would be swallowed up within a week if he tried to meet these commitments.

He lit a cigar, started the car engine and drove slowly back to Paradise City. During the drive, his mind was active. Something had to be done, and done fast.

Kramer hadn't been known as a dangerous criminal for nothing. Okay, he told himself, savagely chewing on his cigar, he had been financially wiped out. Well, he wasn't too old to start again, but how? That was the question . . . how? To make four million dollars when you are sixty years old wanted some doing . . . an impossible task . . . unless . . .

His slate grey eyes narrowed. His heavy sunburned face with its square jaw, lipless mouth and long thick nose set in a hard, expressionless mask while his brain poked and probed for a way out of this financial hole.

He arrived back at the villa to find Helene preparing to go out. She looked anxiously at him.

"Did you find out why he did it?" she asked as Kramer came heavily into the lounge.

"He got caught short," Kramer said curtly. "He was a little too smart . . . like the rest of them. Look, baby, run along. I've things to think about."

"You mean he went bust?" Helene stared: her green-blue eyes horrified. She had always regarded Solly Lucas as a kind of financial wizard. It was unbelievable to her that Solly of all people could lose his money.

Kramer grinned mirthlessly.

"That's about it. He went bust all right."

"Why didn't he come to us? We could have helped him," Helene said, wringing her hands. "Poor Solly! Why didn't he come to us?"

"Are you going out?" Kramer said, his face darkening. "I've things to do."

"I thought I'd drive down town . . . the mink stole. The girl wanted me to approve the skins."

Kramer hesitated for a brief moment. This wasn't the time to buy a mink stole, he told himself, but he had promised it to Helene. There would still be time to cancel the order if things got really rugged. He patted her arm.

"Go ahead. I'll be seeing you," and he walked into his

study: a big room with books, a desk, three lounging chairs
and a view of the rose garden.

He closed the door and sat behind his desk. He lit a cigar.
He heard Helene drive away in her two-seater Jag. He had
two hours, possibly more, to consider his position before
Helene returned. The two coloured servants who ran the
house wouldn't disturb him. He sat motionless, his slate
grey eyes fixed in a blank stare at the curling smoke of his
cigar. The hands of his desk clock moved on. There was no
sound in the room except for the faint ticking of the clock
and Kramer's heavy breathing. He sat there, a brooding
evil genius, determined to win back his lost fortune if he
could only think of the means.

He had been thinking for the best part of an hour when
he abruptly got to his feet. He walked over to the window
and looked out onto the neat lawn and the massed beds of
roses without seeing them. Then he crossed the room, unlocked a drawer in his desk, and took from it a cheap
manilla file. He opened the file and looked thoughtfully at
a number of Press-cuttings that were neatly clipped into the
file. He fingered the cuttings, his heavy face sullen in
thought. He finally closed the file and put it back into the
drawer.

Moving silently, he went to the door of the study and
easing it open, he listened. Faintly, down the passage he
could hear the murmur of voices of Sam and Martha, his
servants, conversing in the kitchen. He closed the door,
went to his desk, searched in the top right-hand desk drawer
until he found a small, shabby address book. He sat down
and consulted the book.

He finally found the telephone number he wanted. He
told the telephone operator he wanted San Francisco. He
gave the number which he read from the book. The operator
said she would call him back.

He replaced the receiver, stubbed out his cigar and leaned
back in the desk chair. His face was now a stony expressionless mask: his eyes were very bleak.

There was a long delay, but finally the operator called
him.

"Your party is now on the line," she told him. "The number has been changed." She sounded irritated that she should have been put to so much trouble.

Kramer was listening to the clicks on the line. He heard a man say, "Hello? Who's that?"

He said, "I want to talk to Moe Zegetti."

The man said, "This is Zegetti. Who's calling?"

"I didn't recognize your voice, Moe," Kramer said. "I guess it is a long time . . . seven years, isn't it?"

"Who's that?" The man's voice sharpened.

"Who do you imagine it is?" Kramer said with a wolfish grin. "Long time no see, Moe. How are you?"

"Jim! For Pete's sake! Is that you, Jim?"

"Who else do you imagine it is?" Kramer asked.

Moe Zegetti could scarcely believe he was listening to the voice of Big Jim Kramer. It was as astonishing to him as if he had been told the President of the United States was calling him.

For fifteen years, Moe had been Kramer's right-hand man. Moe had been responsible for at least twenty major bank robberies that had been blueprinted by Kramer. During those fifteen years, Moe had come to be regarded by the police and the underworld as one of the top craftsmen in the business. There seemed nothing he couldn't turn his hand to. Among many other things, he could open the most complicated safe, pick a pocket, forge a hundred-dollar bill, cope with the most foolproof burglar alarm, drive a get-away car and nick a playing card edgeways on at fifteen yards with a .38 automatic. But in spite of his technical skill, Moe lacked organizing ability. When he was given a blueprint for a job, he would achieve success, but put him on his own, let him plan his own *modus operandi* and he was hopelessly lost.

He discovered this depressing fact when Kramer retired. Moe attempted a fairly simple job on his own, based on his own planning. He was immediately picked up and he spent six heartbreaking years in San Quentin penitentiary, and because the police were certain that he had been responsible for so many brilliant bank robberies, the word went out to the warders and Moe had a very rough time.

He came out of the penitentiary a broken man. By now he was forty-eight, running to fat and with an inflamed kidney, acquired from one of the brutal beatings he had taken in prison. He was now only the shadow of the man known as the smartest technician in the rackets.

Although he had made an impressive sum of money during his career as a criminal, he had always been a soft touch and a reckless gambler. He came out of prison without a nickel, but at least he had a refuge to go to . . . his mother.

Doll Zegetti, aged seventy-two, ran two de luxe brothels in San Francisco. She was a massive, handsome woman who adored her son as he adored her. She was shocked at the change in him when he came to her ornate apartment on the day of his release from San Quentin. She realized his spirit and his nerve had been shattered, and if he was to get back onto his feet again, he would need very careful nursing.

She set him up in a three-room apartment and told him to rest. This Moe was glad to do. He spent long hours, sitting in a chair at the window, watching the shipping in the harbour and doing nothing. The very thought of turning his hand to crime again made his blood run cold.

This state of affairs continued for eighteen months. Often Moe thought of Kramer who he worshipped, admiring him for being so smart as to get out of the rackets with four million dollars before the chopper fell. It never crossed his mind to put the bite on Kramer. The idea that his late boss might help him some way or other did not occur to him.

Then things began to go wrong for Doll. Captain O'Hardy of the Vice-Squad retired and a new man climbed into the saddle. He was Captain Capshaw, a lean, hard-eyed Quaker who hated prostitution and was no man to be offered a bribe. Within three weeks of his appointment, he had slammed both Doll's houses shut and had arrested most of her girls. Doll was suddenly without an income and heavily in debt. The blow seemed to paralyse her. She fell ill and was now in hospital undergoing certain tests: their mystery terrified Moe.

With his weekly income from Doll cut off, Moe was in trouble. He moved from the three-room apartment and took a room in a sordid tenement block close to the 'Frisco docks. Before looking for a job, he pawned his clothes and the various possessions he had collected, then faced with the prospects of starving, he reluctantly looked for work. Eventually he became a waiter in a small Italian restaurant. The one smart thing Moe did was to inform the 'Frisco telephone exchange of his changing telephone numbers. It was because of this foresight that Kramer found him.

It took several minutes before Moe could realize that it was really Kramer at the other end of the line. He had to control his excitement as he said, "Big Jim! I never thought to hear your voice again!"

Kramer's familiar rumbling laugh came over the line.

"How are you, Moe? How are you doing . . . pretty good?"

Moe looked down the narrow restaurant with its close-packed greasy-topped tables, at the steamed-up windows and the ruins of many meals waiting for him to clear. He caught sight of himself in the big fly-blown mirror behind the bar: a short, fat man with a mop of greying thick hair, heavy eyebrows, a white sweating face and dark, scared eyes.

"I'm doing all right," he lied. It would never do to let Big Jim know the mess he was in. He knew Big Jim: he had no use for failures. He glanced at Fransioli, his boss, who was counting the cash, then lowering his voice, he went on, "I have my own business now . . . doing fine."

"That's swell," Kramer said. "Look, Moe, I want to see you. Something has come up . . . could be you'll be interested. It's big money . . . when I say big, that's what I mean. Your end could be a quarter of a million bucks. You interested?"

Moe broke out in a sweat.

"This line's not so hot," he said. "What was that again?"

"I said something has come up," Kramer said, speaking

more slowly. "Your end could be a quarter of a million bucks."

Moe closed his eyes. He suddenly was back in the small cell again, crouching against the far wall as two warders came in, grinning. Wrapped around their massive fists were leather belts. He felt the bile rise in his mouth and the memory of the awful beating he had taken set his mind quivering with fear.

"Hello?" Kramer's voice was now impatient. "You still there, Moe?"

"Sure . . . sounds good. Just what is it, Jim?"

"I can't talk on an open line," Kramer said, an edge to his voice. "I want you out here. We'll talk about it. You know where I am . . . Paradise City. When can you come?"

Moe looked with dismay at his shabby clothes. The other suit he owned was now nearly as shabby. He knew the way Big Jim lived. The fare to Paradise City would be around twenty dollars, and he hadn't twenty dollars. There were no days off at the restaurant: he even worked on Sundays, but something long forgotten stirred inside him. Big Jim and a quarter of a million dollars! Big Jim had never steered him wrong!

Lowering his voice so that Fransioli couldn't hear what he was saying, he said, "I could get over there on Saturday. I'm pretty tied up right now."

"What's today . . . Tuesday? This is urgent, Moe. I want you sooner than that. You come Thursday. You don't pick up this kind of money every day. How about Thursday?"

Moe wiped the sweat out of his eyes with the back of his hand.

"Anything you say, Jim. Sure . . . I'll be along Thursday."

He became aware that Fransioli was listening now and staring balefully at him.

"Fly in," Kramer said. "I'll be at the airport. There's a flight arriving at eleven-forty-three. We can drive out here and have lunch. Okay?"

This would cost him his job, Moe was thinking, but to be hooked up with Big Jim again!

"I'll be there."

"Fine . . . be seeing you, Moe," and the connection was cut.

Slowly Moe replaced the receiver.

Fransioli, smelling of sweat and sweet wine, came over to him.

"What's all this about?" he demanded. "You thinking of going some place?"

"It's nothing," Moe said, wiping his hands on his dirty apron. "Just a drunk. I knew him years ago. He's stupid in the head."

Fransioli stared suspiciously at him.

"Just so long as you aren't," he said and began to wash glasses.

The rest of the day passed very slowly for Moe. The magic words "a quarter of a million dollars" burned into his brain.

Around four o'clock, Moe returned to his bed-sitting-room. He had two clear hours before returning to the restaurant. He moved like a man in a desperate hurry. He tore off his greasy clothes and washed himself. He ran an electric razor over his dark, sprouting beard. He put on a clean shirt and his best suit. While he was changing he was aware of the strident sound of a transistor radio blaring off-beat music in the apartment below.

He paid no attention to the noise, but hurriedly completed his toilet. He ran down the four flights of stairs and into the hot street. A quick walk brought him to the trolley-bus stop. On the way, he had paused to buy a small bunch of violets. Every day, he bought the violets for Doll. They were her favourite flower.

The trolley-bus took him to the door of the hospital. He climbed the steps, walked along the corridors until he finally reached the long, depressing ward full of ageing women, ill or dying, who watched his long walk down the polished aisle until he reached the bed in which his mother was lying.

He was always shocked when he saw her again. She seemed to be shrinking. Her handsome, strong face was turning the colour of old ivory. Pain had made deep lines around her mouth, and now for the first time, he saw a look of defeat in her eyes.

He sat on the hard chair at her side and held her hand. She told him she was getting along pretty well and there was nothing for him to worry about. In a couple of weeks she would be up and about, then she would see what she could do to fix Captain Capshaw. There was still a faint fighting light in her eyes, but Moe had a horrible feeling that she would never set her big, firm feet on the floor again.

He told her about the telephone call he had had from Kramer.

"I don't know what it's all about," he said, "but you know Big Jim . . . he's never steered me wrong."

Doll drew in a long, slow breath. The grinding pain in her left side became as nothing at this news. She had always admired Big Jim who had often come to her houses, brutally treating her girls, and then drinking half a bottle of Scotch with her before leaving. He was a man! Shrewd, clever and very, very smart! A man who had got out of the rackets with four million dollars, and now he wanted her son!

"You see him, Moe," she said. "Big Jim's never made a mistake! A quarter of a million! Think of it!"

"Yes . . . if Big Jim says a thing, he means it." Moe shifted uneasily. "But, Momma, I can't go looking this way . . . he wants me to fly down there. I haven't got the money. I – I told him I was doing fine . . . owned my own restaurant. You know Jim. I couldn't tell him the mess we're in."

Doll realized the sense of this and she nodded.

"I've got the money, Moe," she said. "When you go down there, you've gotta go in style." She reached into her bedside locker and took from it a black crocodile bag, one of her very few remaining possessions she had managed to hold on to. She took from it an envelope and gave it to him. "Use this, Moe. Get yourself a good suit: fit yourself up. You'll want pyjamas, shirts and stuff like that. Get yourself a good-looking suitcase. Big Jim notices things like that."

Moe peered into the envelope. His eyes widened when he saw it contained ten one-hundred-dollar bills.

"For Pete's sake, Momma! Where did this come from?"

Doll grinned.

"I've had it some time. It's my emergency money, son. Now it's yours. Spend it carefully. There's nothing to follow."

"But you need it, Momma!" Moe was still staring at the money as if hypnotized. "I can't take it. You'll need every dime you can scrape up if you're going to get well."

Doll pressed her hand to her side. The grinding pain was back again and making her sweat.

"You're going to make a quarter of a million, stupid," she said. "We'll have all the money we need after you've talked to Jim. Take it."

Moe took the money. He went back to the restaurant and told Fransioli he was quitting. Fransioli shrugged. Waiters, he said, came a dime a dozen. He didn't offer to shake hands with Moe at the parting and this upset Moe: these days Moe was easily upset.

He spent all Wednesday buying the things he needed. Then he returned to his sordid little room and spent some time packing the pigskin suitcase he had bought and putting on his new suit. He had had a haircut and a manicure. Staring at himself in the mirror, he scarcely recognized the prosperous-looking man who stared back at him.

Carrying the suitcase, he hurried to the hospital, not forgetting to buy some violets on the way. The Ward Sister told him curtly his mother wasn't receiving visitors this day. She was in a little pain, and it was better not to disturb her.

Moe stared at the slim, blonde girl, a sense of utter desolation and fear clutching at his heart.

"There's nothing badly wrong, is there?" he asked timidly.

"Oh no. She is a little uncomfortable. She is resting. You'll probably be able to see her tomorrow." Nodding, the nurse walked away, casually adjusting her belt, her mind obviously occupied with other things.

Moe hesitated, then slowly walked towards the exit. It wasn't until he reached the street that he realized he was still carrying the bunch of violets. He walked back to the flower seller and gave her the violets.

"Momma isn't so good today," he said. "You have them. I'll get some more tomorrow. She would like you to have them."

Back in his room, he sat on the bed and rested his face in his hands. He remained like that until the shadows lengthened and the room grew dark. He had forgotten how to pray, but he tried. All he could mutter over and over again was, "Sweet Jesus, look after Momma. Take care of her: stay with her. I need her."

It was the best he could do.

When the transistor in the apartment below began its strident noise, he went down to the telephone booth across the street and called the hospital.

A woman's impersonal voice told him his mother was still a little uncomfortable. When he asked to speak to the doctor in charge, he was told he wasn't available.

Moe spent the rest of the evening in a bar. He drank two bottles of Chianti wine and when he finally returned to his room, he was a little drunk.

CHAPTER THREE

On Thursday morning while Kramer was eating ham and eggs and Helene, who never ate breakfast, was pouring him his second cup of coffee, he said casually, "Moe Zegetti is flying down to see me this morning, sweetheart. He'll be staying for lunch."

Helene slopped the coffee as she turned to stare at her husband.

"Who?"

"Moe Zegetti. You remember him, don't you?" Kramer said, not looking at her. He reached for a piece of toast and began to spread butter on it.

"You mean that – that crook? He's just out of jail, isn't he?"

"He's been out close on two years," Kramer said mildly. "He's a good guy. You used to like him, Helene."

Helene sat down abruptly. She had gone a little pale.

"What's he want?"

"Nothing. He's running his own business now," Kramer said, stirring his coffee. "He telephoned me yesterday. He's coming to Paradise City on business. Knowing I was here, he thought he would look me up. Nice to see him again. He's a good guy."

"He's a crook!" Helene said fiercely. "Jim! You promised to stay clear of those hoods. You've got to remember our position! Suppose someone found out an ex-convict has been calling here?"

Kramer controlled his rising temper with difficulty.

"Oh, come on, Helene, relax. He's an old friend. Just because he's been in jail doesn't mean a thing. He's going straight now. I told you . . . he's in business on his own."

Helene fixed her husband with a long, searching stare. He forced himself to meet her eyes and he smiled.

"What kind of business?"

Kramer shrugged.

"I don't know. You ask him when you see him."

"I don't want to see him! I don't want him here!" She drew in a deep breath, and then continued. "Look, Jim, you've been out of the rackets now for five years: you stay out!"

Kramer finished the last morsel of ham and pushed aside his plate. He lit a cigarette.

There was a long pause, then he said, an edge to his voice, "Nobody tells me what to do, Helene, you know that: not even you. Just relax. Moe's coming here for lunch. He's coming because he is an old friend of mine: no other reason . . . so relax."

Helene saw the hard light in the slate grey eyes and she flinched. She had always been a little afraid of her husband when he looked this way. She knew she was getting no younger, that she was putting on weight, and when she examined her face in the mirror each morning, she was distressed by her fading looks. Kramer, although sixty, was still vigorous and lusty. So far he hadn't looked at other women, but she had the growing fear that if she wasn't careful how she handled him, he might look elsewhere.

As she stood up, she forced a smile.

"All right, darling. I'll fix something nice for him. I didn't mean anything. It just worried me that he should turn up here . . . out of the past."

Kramer studied her.

"There's nothing to worry about," he said and got to his feet. "Well, I'm off to the airport. We'll get back around half past twelve. See you, sweetheart." He patted her behind with a heavy hand, brushed his lips across her cheek and went out of the room.

Helene went back to her chair and sat down. Her legs felt suddenly weak. Moe Zegetti! Her mind went back to those years when Moe was Jim's right-hand man. She had nothing against Moe personally: it was what he stood for that frightened her. An ex-convict! Here in Paradise City when she and Jim had won their way into Paradise City's society and were regarded as two nice, respectable people, always wanted when a party was thrown. Suppose someone found out that Moe had had lunch with them? She put her hand to her face. What was Jim thinking of?

Inspector Jay Dennison and Special Agent Tom Harper, both of the F.B.I., were waiting impatiently in the airport lobby for their flight to Washington to be announced.

Dennison, a burly, muscular man with a ginger moustache and a bridge of freckles across his thick nose, was getting on for forty-eight: a sound, hard-working Federal Agent whose headquarters was in Paradise City. Harper looked a stripling beside the inspector. He was tall, lean and some twenty years the inspector's junior and making his way. Even Dennison, who was a hard task master, was satisfied with the way Harper was shaping. The two men had grown to like each other, and now Harper was planning to marry Dennison's daughter.

It was while they were sitting away from the swirl of the crowd that Dennison suddenly put his hand on Harper's arm.

"Look who's blown in," he said. "That fat little punk just passing through the arrival gate."

Harper spotted the short fat man with greying hair and a fat, round, sweating face who had just walked into the lobby. He meant nothing to Harper, who looked inquiringly at his chief.

Dennison got to his feet.

"Play this gently," he said. "This punk interests me."

The two men moved casually after the little man who was carrying a brand new suitcase. As he reached the double glass doors leading out into the parking lot where lines of taxis and cars waited, Dennison paused.

"That's Moe Zegetti," he said, watching Moe as he stood looking to right and left uncertainly. "Remember him? You wouldn't have met him . . . before your time, but you'll remember his record."

"So that's Zegetti," Harper said, his lean face showing his interest. "Sure, I remember his record. He was Kramer's stooge and he was one of the top boys in the rackets at one time. He went down for six years and has been out two:

since then he has been behaving himself. Looks as if he's done himself pretty well. That's a nice suit he's got on."

Dennison glanced at Harper and nodded approvingly.

"That's the punk. Now I wonder what he is doing here."

"Look . . . to your left. There's Kramer himself!"

A voice distorted by the loudspeaker system announced that all passengers for Washington should go at once to Gate 5.

The two Federal Agents paused long enough to see Kramer wave a big hand and Moe Zegetti start towards him before they reluctantly turned away and walked with the crowd to Gate 5.

"Kramer and Zegetti . . . an unbeatable combination," Dennison said thoughtfully. "Could mean trouble."

"You don't imagine Kramer is coming out of retirement?" Harper said. "He wouldn't be that crazy with all his money."

Dennison shrugged.

"I don't know. I've been asking myself why Solly Lucas shot himself. He looked after Kramer's money. Well, we'll keep tabs on them. I'll alert the boys when we're on the plane. I've waited twenty-one years to get Kramer. If he's coming out of retirement . . . this could be my chance."

Unaware that he was being watched, Moe started across the tarmac towards Kramer who came to meet him. As they approached, both men looked searchingly at each other, curious to see any change since last they met some seven years ago.

To Moe, Kramer looked bronze and fit, although a lot heavier. He had lost that restless, springy walk that Moe was familiar with, but this didn't exactly surprise him. After all, Big Jim must be sixty now, and at that age, you don't walk like a young man. Kramer was wearing a nigger brown suede golfing jacket, fawn gaberdine slacks and a white peak cap. He seemed to be prosperous and relaxed.

Kramer noted that Moe was overweight and pale. He looked unhealthy and soft. This discovery made Kramer look more searchingly at Moe. He then became aware of the uneasy, almost frightened expression in the dark eyes and the nervous way Moe's lips tightened and slackened. On the credit side, Kramer thought, Moe looked prosperous enough. He couldn't have slipped too far back to wear a suit like the one he was wearing.

"Good to see you again," Kramer said, grasping Moe's hand. "How are you?"

Aware of the iron grip, Moe stiffened his own flabby grip. He said he was fine and how good it was to see Kramer again. The two men walked over to a gleaming black Cadillac.

"This yours, Jim?" Moe asked, impressed.

"Yeah, but I'm trading it in for the new model," Kramer said, unable to resist boasting. "Get in. Helene is preparing a special lunch for you. I don't want my ears knocked off for being late."

Kramer asked after Doll as he drove onto the highway. Moe told him of the situation.

Kramer was shocked. He was fond of Doll.

"She'll pull through," he said. "She's tough, Moe. You see . . . this kind of thing happens to us all sooner or later, but we come through, and so will she."

Casually, he asked about San Quentin. Out of the corner of his eye, he saw Moe's hands turn into fists. Moe said in a tight strangled voice that it had been pretty rugged.

"I guess," Kramer said soberly and shook his head. This was something that haunted his dreams. He knew he had escaped San Quentin by the skin of his teeth. "Well, it's behind you. That's the way to look at it . . . it's behind you."

During the rest of the twenty-mile drive, the two men chatted about this and that, recalling the past, mentioning names of people they had known, the places they had visited together. There was no talk as to why Kramer wanted to see Moe.

Lunch passed off fairly well. Helene had provided a good meal, if a trifle heavy, but Moe was quick to realize that his visit wasn't welcome by her, and this upset him a little.

Half-way through the meal, Helene asked him bluntly what he was doing now.

Moe said he had a restaurant and it was doing all right.

"Then what are you doing in Paradise City?" Helene demanded, scarcely concealing her hostility.

As Moe hesitated uneasily, Kramer cut in, "He's looking for another restaurant. It's a great idea. We could do with a good Italian restaurant in Paradise City."

After lunch, Helene said she was going down town and then on to the Bridge Club.

When the two men were alone, Kramer said, "Let's go into my study, Moe. I want to talk to you."

Moe, who had been enormously impressed by Kramer's house, garden, the elaborate furnishing and décor, followed Kramer into the study. He stared through the big window at the rose garden and shook his head enviously.

"You've certainly got yourself a place, Jim," he said as Kramer waved him to a chair. "You must be pretty pleased with it."

Kramer sat down, pushed a box of cigars towards Moe, before helping himself.

"It's okay," he said, paused and then went on, "You remember Solly Lucas?"

Moe frowned, then nodded.

"Sure. What's he doing these days . . . still working for you, Jim?"

Kramer sat forward, his fleshy face granite hard.

"He shot himself a couple of weeks ago. He did the job before I could get to him."

Moe flinched and sat back in his chair, staring at Kramer.

"Yeah," Kramer went on. "He put me in the hole for four million bucks. This is between you and me, Moe. Helene doesn't know, and I don't want her to know." He grinned mirthlessly. "I guess you have more dollars right now than I have cents."

Moe was so stunned that he could think of nothing to say. He just stared at Kramer. Big Jim . . . taken for four million bucks! It was unbelievable!

"I've got to make myself another lump of money," Kramer went on. "It can be done, but I'll need help. You're the first guy I thought of. You and I have always worked well together. We can still pull off a big job."

Still Moe could find nothing to say.

"I have an idea," Kramer said, after a pause. "It's worth a heap of dough if we play it right. I'll organize and handle it, but I need you. Don't look so scared, Moe. I'll tell you this: there's no risk! I promise you that! No risk . . . understand?" He looked searchingly at Moe. "I wouldn't have called you in, Moe, if there was any chance of trouble. I know how tough San Quentin must have been. Listen . . . I give you my word you'll never go back there if you work with me. There's no risk in this job, otherwise, at my age, I wouldn't be sticking my neck out or risking yours."

Moe suddenly lost all his fears. If Big Jim said he could make him a quarter of a million dollars with no risk, incredible as it sounded, that's what Big Jim would do. During the fifteen years that Moe had worked with Kramer, he had never had any fear of trouble. He still had utter faith in Kramer: when Kramer promised something with that bleak look in his eyes . . . it was a promise.

"What's the deal then?" Moe asked, excitement showing on his face.

Kramer stretched his long legs and blew a cloud of rich-smelling smoke towards the ceiling.

"Have you ever heard of John Van Wylie?"

Looking bewildered, Moe shook his head.

"He is a Texas oilman. You may not believe this, for it is hard to believe, but he is worth more than a billion dollars."

Moe blinked.

"No guy can be worth that much," he said. "A billion dollars! How can a guy be worth all that dough?"

"His father struck oil back in the nineties," Kramer said. "The old man bought acres of land in Texas in the pioneer days for a song. Wherever he probed for oil, he found it. He never once hit a dry hole . . . imagine that! His son took over when the old man died, and he was a much smarter business man than his father. For every dollar his father made, John Van Wylie had the touch to turn that dollar into ten dollars. I tell you, now he is worth more than a billion dollars."

Moe mopped his sweating face.

"I've heard of such things happening, but I've never believed it."

"I've been keeping tabs on Van Wylie for years," Kramer said. "The guy fascinates me." He got to his feet and unlocked a drawer in his desk. He lifted out a file of newspaper clippings. "Every one of these clippings refers to the Van Wylie family. I now know nearly as much about them as they know about themselves." He dropped the file back into the drawer and returned to his chair and sat down. "Now and then, I amuse myself working out schemes to make big money, but I didn't think I would have to get back into the game again. Well, I have to get back and these ideas of mine are now going to pay off." He tapped ash off his cigar and then went on, "Van Wylie lost his wife . . . cancer. There is a daughter. She happens to look like her mother. I know for a fact that she is the one thing in Van Wylie's life that means anything."

Kramer gazed for a long moment at the glowing end of his cigar, then he said, "Van Wylie has everything any man needs. He can't possibly spend all the money he has made. He values nothing because if he loses something, he has the money to replace it." A long pause, then Kramer said, speaking softly, "but he can't replace his daughter."

Moe said nothing. He waited, aware that his heart was beginning to thump uneasily.

Kramer leaned forward, his face harsh, his eyes glittering. "So we snatch his daughter and make a nice, safe private deal with him for four million dollars."

Moe stiffened. His heart skipped a beat. His dark eyes open very wide.

"Wait a minute, Jim!" His voice shot up a note. "That's a Federal rap! We could land up in the gas chamber!"

"Do you imagine I haven't thought of that?" Kramer asked impatiently. "I've told you: this is going to be a nice, safe, private deal and that's what it is going to be. Think about it for a moment. Van Wylie loses his daughter . . . the only possession he sets any value to. Four million dollars is peanuts to a man like Van Wylie. Imagine what you would do if some hood snatched your daughter and offered to return her, safe and sound, for twenty bucks. You'd pay up, wouldn't you? You'd be glad to have her back for chick feed. Would you call in the Feds? You damn well wouldn't! You'd be glad to do a deal. Four million dollars to a man of Van Wylie's wealth is chick feed! Can't you see that? He gets his daughter back, no fuss, no trouble and he loses what to you would be twenty bucks."

But Moe wasn't convinced. He had a horror of any job that carried the death sentence.

"But when he gets her back, he'll stick the Feds on to us," he said, thumping his fists on his fat knees. "A guy like that isn't going to part with all that money without trying to hit back."

"You're wrong," Kramer said. "I'll convince him if he tries anything smart like that, no matter how carefully the girl is guarded, one day someone will arrive with a shotgun and that will be the end of his daughter. I'll put the fear of God into him. I'll convince him that sooner or later she will be fixed even if it takes a couple of years. He'll see reason. You can't guard a girl for years. He'll see that."

Moe considered this for a long moment, then he nodded.

"Well, okay, Jim. I've always relied on you. If you say so, then it is so." He hesitated, then asked, "Just what do you want me to do?"

"You'll have the easy end of it," Kramer said. "You'll handle the snatch . . . not alone, of course. We'll need two other guys. That's where I'm relying on you. I used to know plenty of punks who could help out, but I've lost touch now. We need a couple of young, tough kids with good nerves. Their cut will be five grand . . . no need to throw our money around. For five grand, you should be able to dig up someone."

Moe was as out of touch as Kramer with the shadowy people of the underworld, but he knew this would be fatal to admit. Kramer wasn't parting with a quarter of a million for nothing. Moe knew Big Jim. So long as you delivered you were in, but if you hesitated or admitted you didn't know, you were out.

His mind worked swiftly. He had a sudden inspiration.

"I know a couple of kids who might do . . . the Cranes. Yeah, come to think of it, they're dead right for this job."

Kramer sucked in smoke and exhaled it.

"The Cranes? Who are they?"

"They live in the apartment below mine. They are pretty wild. They're twins: brother and sister. You know these beatnik kids . . . he runs a gang. They'll want handling, but they have the nerve."

Kramer grinned. He had been handling wild ones all his life.

"I'll handle them," he said. He flicked ash into the ash-tray. "Tell me about them. What do they do for a living?"

"Nothing," Moe said. "They never have done anything. Like I said, they are wild ones." He paused to stub out his cigar. "Their father was a gunman, sticking up small shops or out-of-the-way gas stations, caught their mother in bed with some jerk. He was drunk at the time and he killed them both. He was sent away for fifteen years. He hanged himself after three months in a cell. Their mother was one of the smartest shoplifters in the racket. She took the kids along with her and they got better at the game than she did. They were ten years of age when they lost their parents. They lived rough, stole their food and kept clear of the cops and the do-gooders. These kids are smart. They have never been caught. They haven't a police record. Now they are running this gang of young beatniks. They put the bite on anyone they can blackmail. The girl dangles her sex and when a sucker falls for her, the boy arrives and shakes him down for his last dime . . . this boy is very tough. Now I guess they're ripe for a big job. They have nerve, guts and they don't scare. It's an idea, Jim, to have a girl in on this caper. She could prove useful."

Kramer thought for a long moment, then he nodded.

"I'll come up to 'Frisco and meet them," he said. "You fix it, Moe. If I think they're right, we'll use them. Okay?"

"I'll talk to them," Moe said. "When they hear you're behind this setup, they'll fall over themselves to get on the gravy train."

Kramer grinned.

"Of course they will, but don't tell them what the setup is, Moe. I want to see them first. Just tell them they have the chance to work for Big Jim Kramer."

Moe looked admiringly at Kramer.

"I'll tell them," he said.

Chita Crane leaned against a lamp-post, indifferent to the slight drizzle of rain, a cigarette between her full, red-painted lips, her large dark eyes fixed with a concentrated stare at the entrance to the Giza Club, across the street.

The time was a little after three o'clock in the morning. Very soon now, the mugs would be coming out. One of them, and it had only to be one, would notice her and would come over. He would be a little drunk or maybe very drunk. He would offer her a lift in his car.

Chita was above average height with broad shoulders, a bust development that would make any man stare, slim hips and long legs. She wore black leather trousers, shiny and greasy from constant wear, and a black leather wind-cheater, on the back of which was painted in white, a realistic-looking Crane-fly or to give it its more popular name: a Daddy Longlegs. This outfit was the uniform both she and Riff, her brother, always wore. They were known among the gangs in their district as the Leatherjackets which, as most people know, are the larvae of the Crane-fly.

When Chita could be bothered, she bleached her dark hair blonde, but more often than not, her hair was a dirty-looking, streaky blonde-black. She had high cheekbones, large blue-black eyes and a well-shaped nose. No one could call her beautiful nor even pretty, but she was sensually attractive to men. Her eyes, old in wickedness and sexual promise, had a magnetic attraction. She was, like her brother, cruel, ruthless and vicious. It is always hard to accept the fact that anyone could have no redeeming feature, but it would be hard to find a redeeming feature in either of the Cranes. Both of them were habitual liars, dishonest and treacherous. They were also selfish, mean and utterly anti-social. Perhaps the one good thing – if you could call it that – in their make-up that someone could point to was their quite extraordinary love for each other. They were identical twins: there was a bond between them that withstood all their quarrelling and their constant fights, and they often fought like animals: Chita giving as good as she got. But if one of them fell ill which was seldom, or got into trouble which was often, the other was always there, giving support no matter how tough the spot. They completely relied on each other: they shared good luck with the bad and it was unthinkable to them if one had a dollar, it wouldn't be automatically shared with the other.

Across the street, standing out of sight in a dark alley was Riff Crane. He was a few inches taller than his sister. His high cheekbones and his big glittering dark eyes were like those of his sister's, but he had had his nose broken in a fight when he was a kid, and some months ago, an enemy had caught him unawares and had cut his face open with a razor from his right eye down to his jawbone. These two scars gave him a vicious, frightening appearance of which he was proud. Chita and he had laid a trap for the man who had slashed him. The score had been successfully settled. The man was now being led around by his wife, half blind and stupid from repeated kicks to his head. Both Chita and Riff always wore ski-ing boots. They went well with their uniform and were terrible weapons in a street fight.

A man suddenly appeared in the doorway of the night club. He looked to right and left, stared at Chita, then started off down the street, his hands in his pockets.

Chita watched him go indifferently. The exodus had begun: sooner or later, some mug would come over to her. She saw her brother flick his glowing cigarette end into the street and move further back into the shadows.

Men and women began to emerge from the night club. Car doors slammed: cars drove away. Still Chita waited. Then a small man, wearing a raincoat and a slouch hat came up the stairs from the night club and paused in the doorway. Chita eyed him with interest and she lit another cigarette, holding the match cupped in her hand to light her face.

The little guy stared across the street at her, seemed to hesitate, then he came over. Chita's experienced eyes noted the quality of the raincoat, the hand-made shoes and the glitter of a gold strap watch. This could be the mug she was waiting for.

The little guy grinned at her as he approached. He had a cocky, knowing air about him. He moved lightly: his thin, foxy face was sun-tanned as if he spent much of his time out of doors.

"Hello, baby," he said, pausing beside her. "Are you waiting for someone?"

Chita let smoke drift down her nostrils. Then she gave him her wide, professional smile.

"Hello, Mac," she said. "If I'm waiting for someone, looks like I've found him, doesn't it?"

The little guy examined her carefully. What he saw seemed to please him.

"That's right: suppose we get out of the rain?" he said. "I have a car over there. Suppose you and me go some place quiet and private? We could have lots to talk about."

Chita laughed. She arched her breasts at him and lifted her dark eyebrows invitingly.

"Sounds like an idea: how private and where?"

"How's about a hotel, baby?" The little guy winked. "I have money to burn. Do you know a quiet little joint we could go to?"

This was easy . . . almost too easy. Chita allowed herself to hesitate before saying, "Well . . . if that's what you want, honey, it's okay with me. I know a place. I'll show you."

She flicked her glowing cigarette high into the air. This was a pre-arranged signal to Riff, letting him know where she was taking the mug.

The little guy owned a Buick convertible. They got in and as Chita settled herself beside the little guy, he said, "That's an off-beat get-up you have on. Suits you. What's the idea of the Daddy Longlegs?"

"It's my signature tune," Chita said. She was already bored with this little man. She only hoped he had a wallet full of money. She eyed the gold strap watch. That, at least, would be worth her trouble.

Five minutes later they were booking into a shady hotel on the waterfront. The reception clerk, a dirty, elderly man, gave Chita a sly wink and she winked back. Both knew that within a few minutes, Riff would be arriving.

They went upstairs and into a fair sized room in which was a double bed, two armchairs, a toilet basin and a threadbare carpet.

Chita sat on the bed and smiled at the little guy who took off his raincoat and hat. He hung them on a peg at the back of the door. He wore a custom made dark suit. He had the appearance of a man of money.

"I'd like my present, honey," Chita said. "Thirty bucks."

The little guy gave her an amused smile and moved to the window. He pushed aside the dirty curtain and peered down into the rain-soaked street. He was in time to see Riff get off his motor-cycle, lift it up on to its stand and then start across the street towards the hotel.

"What are you looking at?" Chita asked, her voice sharpening. "Come here . . . I want my present."

The little guy gave her an amused smile and moved to the window.

"No present, baby," he said. "Nothing for you. I want to meet your brother."

Chita stared at him.

"My brother? What the hell are you talking about?"

"Last week, you picked up a pal of mine," the little guy said. "You brought him here. You and your brother skinned him and then your jerk of a brother beat him up. Now it's my turn . . ."

Chita eyed the little guy with sudden alert interest. He looked harmless enough. He was small boned, light weight and even fragile. Riff could kill him with one punch.

"Be your age, Sawn-off," she said contemptuously. "We don't want trouble, but you'll have it if you don't watch out. Riff could handle ten like you. If you don't want to land up in the casualty ward, hand over your wallet and your watch. I'll see Riff doesn't hurt you."

The little guy sniggered. He seemed to be enjoying himself.

"The Leatherjackets! Two dumb vicious kids who can't earn a dime unless they use force. Baby, this has been piling up for you both for a long, long time. Now you're going to get it."

As he spoke the bedroom door swung open and Riff came in. Usually when he entered this sordid room, Chita had taken off her clothes and was lying naked on the bed, and this gave him the chance of acting as the indignant brother. Seeing her sitting on the bed, fully dressed and staring at the little guy who stood in the centre of the room, still smiling, brought Riff to an abrupt standstill.

"Come on in, punk," the little guy said. "I've been sweating to meet you."

Riff looked at Chita who shrugged impatiently.

"Don't ask me," she said, but she was a little uneasy. "I guess he's nuts."

Riff moved into the room and shut the door. There was a watchful, alert expression in his eyes. His big fists dangled loosely at his sides.

"Okay, Mac," he said. "The watch and the wallet. Snap it up. I want some sleep tonight even if you don't."

"I'm in no hurry to sleep," the little guy said and sniggered. He seemed to be having a wonderful time and his lack of fear sparked off Riff's vicious temper.

"Snap it up!" he snarled and began to move forward.

The little guy backed away quickly until he was against the far wall.

"You want my wallet?" he asked and put his hand inside his coat.

"Watch him!" Chita said sharply.

Riff paused. The little guy had a gun in his hand. He pointed it at Riff.

"Hi, sucker!" the little guy said cheerfully. "You didn't expect to run into anything like this, did you?"

Riff snarled at him.

"You let off that heater and you'll be in lots of trouble," he said.

He made a quick feinting movement to the right and then charged the little guy. Chita caught her breath. It seemed a mad thing to do.

She saw Riff reel back and clap his hands to his face as at the same time, she smelt the burning fumes of ammonia. Riff fell on his knees, his hands scrubbing at his eyes and howling like an animal in pain. Sniggering, the little guy watched him. As Chita started to her feet, he swung around and aimed the ammonia gun at her. She just managed to cover her face with her hands as the burst of ammonia hit her. She saved her eyes, but she drew in a lungful of the scorching fumes. Screaming, she rolled from the bed onto the floor.

The little guy regarded his handiwork with satisfaction. He put the gun back into his pocket. He took his raincoat from the peg and put it on. Then he slapped his hat on his head at a jaunty angle. He paused for a long moment to watch the Cranes writhing like cut worms on the floor, then he let himself out of the room and went jauntily down to his car.

The Cranes never found out who he was. When the news got around how he had fixed them, those who had suffered at their hands regarded this anonymous little guy as a symbol of justice.

CHAPTER FOUR

Special Agent Abe Mason sat in his car some fifty yards from the entrance to the Regis Court Hotel, a quiet, second-rate hotel in a side street off Van Ness Avenue, San Francisco.

The previous evening, Special Agent Harry Garson had reported to the Field Office that Kramer had arrived at the hotel and had booked in. Since then, Garson and Mason had taken turns to watch the hotel.

Since Kramer had arrived, neither of the agents had seen him. He appeared to be lying doggo. They were satisfied there was no rear exit to the hotel. When Kramer chose to show himself, they wouldn't fail to spot him.

The time by Mason's strap watch was twenty minutes after eleven o'clock. The morning had been unproductive so far, but Mason was trained to patience. Often enough he had sat outside sleezy hotels for days on end without anything happening, but he knew, sooner or later, so long as he remained where he was, something was bound to happen.

At exactly eleven-thirty, his patience was rewarded. A taxi pulled up outside the hotel and Moe Zegetti got out. After paying the cabby, he hurried into the hotel. Mason lifted the mike of his radio-telephone and reported back to Jay Dennison.

"Stick with them, Abe," Dennison said. "I'll send Tom over. When Zegetti comes out, Tom will take care of him. You take care of Kramer."

Two elderly women came down the street and entered the hotel. A little later a woman with a small boy came in a taxi and also entered the hotel.

Mason lit a cigarette and relaxed. These people couldn't have anything to do with Kramer.

A few minutes to midday, a girl and a young man came walking down the street. They looked like twins. The girl, her hair dyed blonde, was wearing a cheap cotton dress, scuffed white shoes and sun-glasses. The young man was dark. He had on bottle green slacks, an open-neck grubby white shirt and over his shoulder he had slung a lightweight fawn-coloured jacket. He also wore sun-glasses. They looked like a couple of students on vacation. Mason gave them a disinterested stare and then dismissed them. Because Moe Zegetti had had the intelligence to insist neither of the Cranes should wear their uniforms, they passed into the hotel without raising the Federal Agent's suspicions.

"The guy in the car across the way," Chita said under her breath. "Could be a dick."

"Yeah, I saw him," Riff said. "Better tell Zegetti. Could mean nothing: could be a private dick on a divorce caper."

They had been told by Moe to go to the first floor, Room 149, knock twice and wait.

There were a few elderly people sitting in the dusty lounge who peered at the Cranes as they walked to the stairs.

A bellhop eyed them, started to get up, but decided it was too much trouble. These two seemed to know where they were going.

They arrived at Room 149, knocked and the door was immediately opened. Moe jerked his thumb and they walked into a comfortably furnished sitting-room with a door opposite them leading into a bedroom.

Big Jim Kramer sat in an armchair by the window, a cigar gripped between his teeth. He examined the Cranes as they moved into the room. They came in cautiously, like animals uneasy in new surroundings. Moe was right. These two were tough. His eyes travelled over Chita: the girl was something . . . that bust of hers! If he had been five years younger, he might have had ideas about her!

Ignoring Kramer, Riff said to Moe, "There's a dick parked outside . . . could be a private eye . . . could be a Fed."

Moe stiffened. His fat face lost a little colour. He looked quickly at Kramer who said quietly. "Forget him. I've got him tagged. The Feds must be interested when Zegetti and I get together . . . they don't miss much." He eased his bulk in the chair, making it creak. "When I'm good and ready, I'll lose him. I've been losing cops for the past forty years."

In their turn, the Cranes examined Kramer. They had read about him in the tabloids when they were kids. They knew him to have been one of the top racketeers in the business: a man who had made six million dollars. Seeing him now, heavy, old with a whisky complexion his suntan couldn't conceal, they were disappointed. They had expected to see a man a lot more lethal-looking than this sixty-year-old hunk of beef, sitting in an armchair and smoking a cigar.

"Sit down, you two," Kramer went on. He stared at Riff who still had a couple of raw blisters on his face where, two weeks ago, the ammonia had burned him. "What's the matter with your face?"

"A whore bit me," Riff said as he sat down.

There was a long pause. Kramer's beefy face turned a dark red and his little eyes snapped.

"Listen to me, you young slob," he snarled, "when I ask a question, you answer up polite . . . hear me?"

"Oh, sure," Riff said indifferently, "but my face belongs to me: it's nothing to you what's the matter with it."

Zegetti eyed Kramer uneasily. In the old days, if some punk talked back to him, Kramer would crush him with a blow in the face, but instead, Kramer shrugged and said, "We're wasting time. Now, listen, you two, I'm fixing a job. I could use you if you want to come in. There's no risk and it's worth five grand. What do you say?"

Chita was aware of the impression she had made on Kramer. She had an instinctive knowledge when she raised lust in men, and she knew she had stirred Kramer's desires.

"No risk?" she asked. "Then what's a cop doing, parked outside?"

"You two little jerks don't know what it is to be famous," Kramer said. "Moe here was one of the top craftsmen in the game and I ran a mob of over five hundred hoods who really knew their business. When Moe and I get together, it's news. The Feds get scared. I said forget it. I'll lose them when I want to. Right now they can sit outside and stew. It won't get them anywhere. When I pull this job, they'll know nothing about it. Do you want the job? It's worth five grand. Make up your minds. If you want it, say so."

Riff touched one of the raw blisters on his face and winced angrily.

"What's the job?"

"You buy it sight unseen," Kramer said. "You don't get the dope until you say you're in, and when you're in, you damn well stay in or you'll have me to reckon with."

The Cranes looked at each other. For the past two weeks they had been having a very bad time. Word had got around how the little guy had fixed them and they had lost face with their gang. The other gangs openly jeered at them, and Riff had been involved in several fights: one of them he had nearly lost. Chita had been pestered on the streets by punks who wouldn't have dared touch her before. Riff had been laid up for a week. The offer of five thousand dollars stunned them. It was more money than they had ever hoped to lay their hands on in their lives. So far they had played it small, but safe. Now, getting themselves hooked up to a fat old square like Kramer could land them into trouble they had so carefully avoided so far.

But the money was too big a temptation. Riff nodded his head at Chita who nodded back.

"Well, okay, we're in," Riff said and taking out a couple of cigarettes, he tossed one to Chita and lit the other for himself. "What's the deal?"

Kramer told them what he had told Moe, but he mentioned no names. He said the girl was the daughter of a wealthy man who would pay ransom without going to the cops.

There was a long pause after Kramer had finished talking. The Cranes looked at each other, then Riff slowly shook his head. To Kramer, he said, "That caper could land us in the gas chamber. Five grand isn't enough. If we're going to risk our necks, we want five grand each."

Kramer's face went a blotchy red.

"I told you! There's no risk!"

"It's a snatch. Something could turn sour," Riff said. "It's hard to keep the Feds out of a caper like this. Ten grand or we don't touch it."

Moe looked anxiously at Kramer. The old man looked as if he was about to burst a blood vessel.

"Then get out!" Kramer spluttered. "The two of you! Out! There are plenty of punks who'd do it at my price!"

Chita moved uneasily, but her brother scowled at her. He said quietly, "For ten grand, we'll do the job, and we'll do it nice and smooth. You won't have any complaints. I promise you that."

"Get out!" Kramer snarled, leaning forward, his face congested. "Hear me! Out!"

"It's not your money," Riff said without moving. "What are you getting excited about? You just raise the ransom a little, and in return you get a hot service."

"It's five grand or nothing!" Kramer said, getting to his feet. His right hand hung near his coat where the bulge of a hidden gun was plain to see.

Riff stared at him for a long moment, his face expressionless, then he stood up.

"Come on, Chita," he said. "We have things to do."

"Wait!" Moe said sharply. Turning to Kramer, he said, "I want a word with you, Jim," and he walked into the bedroom.

After hesitating while he glared at Riff, Kramer stormed into the bedroom, slamming the door.

"What is it?" he snarled.

"Take it easy, Jim," Moe said quietly. "Don't say I didn't warn you. These two are tricky and you're handling them wrong. They are worth ten grand. They'll do the job. We can't afford not to pay them now. They now know we are planning a snatch. They are like snakes. I told you. Give them what they want and they'll do a job, but turn them out now and they'll cross the street and tell that Fed what's cooking. Neither of them have a record . . . but we have. Those two could fix us now. Don't you see that?"

For some seconds, Kramer stood mouthing at Moe, his face purple, his great fists clenching and unclenching. Finally, he said in a voice that shook with rage, "You imagine I'm going to be stood up by a slob like him? I'll get some hood to kill him. I'll . . ."

"Who will you get to do it?" Moe asked. "Neither of us have gunmen to call up now, Jim. If you did find someone, you'd have to pay him, and anyway, it would be too late. Once the Feds know we are planning a snatch, we're through."

Kramer walked slowly and heavily to the window. He turned his back on Moe. He felt a nagging pain under his heart. He hadn't been so worked up in years and this pain scared him. He stood motionless, breathing heavily until he felt the blood gradually leave his face and his heartbeats return to normal.

Moe watched him uneasily, seeing the sag to the heavy shoulders and the furtive hand pressing against the bulky left side.

Kramer turned.

"You really think these slobs can do a job?" he demanded.

"I'm sure of it," Moe said.

Kramer hesitated, drew in a long, deep breath, then suddenly shrugged.

"Well, all right, but if I have any more trouble from them, I'll kill them myself!"

Knowing this was a face-saving boast, Moe nodded.

"That's right, Jim, but right now, let's talk to them again."

They went back into the sitting-room. Riff was lighting another cigarette, his face expressionless. Chita was lolling back in her chair, her eyes closed. Her cheap dress had ridden up a little: she showed the tops of her stockings. As the two men came in, she straightened and pulled down her dress, but not before Kramer had seen the length of her slim, sensual-looking legs.

"We've talked about this," Moe said before Kramer could speak. "You'll get five grand each, but for that money, you'd better do a job."

Riff nodded. His dark eyes lit up, but his face remained expressionless.

"We'll do a job," he said, looking at Kramer. He felt a surge of triumph run through him. He knew that Chita had thought he had gone crazy when he had turned down the first offer. For an uneasy minute, he thought too he had made a mistake, but he had bluffed this old square, and he had pulled it off! "You tell us what to do and we'll do it!"

Kramer sat down. His face was blotchy and he still felt this tugging pain on his left side. He found his eyes kept going to Chita, remembering the glimpse he had had of her white thighs. The more he looked at her, the more her sensual body disturbed him.

"I warn you two," he said, "from now on you do what I tell you. I'm not having any trouble from either of you ... understand?"

Having won his victory, Riff could afford a servile nod of his head.

"You'll have nothing to grumble about," he said. "You can be sure of that."

Kramer stared at him. The expressionless, scarred face, the flat snake's eyes bothered him a little. It was quite a time since he had had to deal with anyone quite as dangerous as this young slob.

"Okay," he said, paused to light a cigar, then when he had it drawing to his satisfaction, he went on, "Here's the plan. The snatch will be easy. I've been checking on the girl. Every Friday morning, she drives alone to San Bernadino for a hairdressing appointment. She then lunches at the Country Club before going back home. She's done this routine run for the past two years. She lives with her father on a big estate out near Arrowhead Lake. There is a three-mile drive from the house down the private road to the San Bernadino highway. The entrance to the private road is guarded by a five-barred gate. There's a telephone by the gate. A caller has to telephone the house and one of the staff releases the lock on the gate and cuts off the electrified wires on the gate with a switch.

"The girl leaves the house around nine o'clock. She reaches the gate at nine-ten." Kramer paused and looked at Chita. "This is your job, so listen carefully. You'll be outside the gate at nine o'clock. You'll have a car. I'll get you one. At nine-ten, you'll open the hood of the car as if you have had a break-down. Don't be too early or you'll have some helpful guy coming to stick his nose into the car. Moe will be with you, but he'll be out of sight. I've checked the place. There's a big clump of shrubs where he can hide and not be far from where you'll be parked. The girl has to get out of her car to open the gate. You'll go up to her, tell her you have a breakdown and will she give you a lift to the nearest service station. She won't refuse you. You're a girl on your own: she won't have anything to be suspicious about. You get in her car and she'll drive you towards San Bernadino. Moe will come out of hiding, get in your car and come after you." Kramer paused and stared at Chita who was sitting forward, listening intently, her elbows on her knees, her face in her hands. "This is where you begin to earn your money. On the way, you have to convince this girl that she has to do exactly what you tell her to do. You'll be provided with the means." He took from his jacket pocket a small flask. "This contains sulphuric acid. Touch this cap at the top of the flask and the acid is projected with considerable force. You tell her if she doesn't do exactly what you tell her, she'll get the acid in her face. Make a demonstration; spray some of the acid on the leatherwork of the car. Be careful how you do it. When she sees the results, she'll behave. I guarantee that!"

Chita nodded as she reached for the flask.

"I'll fix it," she said. "That's easy. I've handled this stuff before."

Kramer and Moe exchanged glances. Moe lifted his eyebrows as if to say, "I told you so, didn't I?"

"You will direct her to Mackling Square car park. This is a big public park and at that hour you won't have any trouble in finding room for the car. Moe will be right behind you. You and the girl will then leave her car and transfer to Moe's car, getting in at the back. You'll have to watch her. She's not likely to make a break for it, but don't relax for a moment ... understand?"

Chita nodded.

Kramer looked over at Moe.

"You'll drive them to Wastelands. You've seen the map and you know where it is. You should get there around mid-day. Okay?"

"Yeah," Moe said.

Chita asked, "Wastelands? What's that?"

Kramer ignored her. He was now looking at Riff.

"Now you get your ears open and listen carefully. This is going to be your end of it. The trick in this is to find a place to hide the girl where no one will think to look for her and also find someone who will arrange about the ransom. None of us is going to contact the father. I've found a fella to do the job. You two ever heard of Victor Dermott?"

Chita said, "There's a guy of that name who writes plays. You don't mean him, do you?"

"That's him," Kramer said. "He has a big reputation: he's known. People think a lot of him. I've picked him to talk to the father. He'll convince him to pay up and to keep the cops off our necks."

"Why the hell should he?" Riff demanded, scowling.

"Because he happens to have a nice-looking wife and a baby," Kramer said, smiling evilly. "You, Moe, the girl and you," he glanced at Chita, "will be in his house. Your job is to put such a scare into this fella he'll do what he is told." Kramer regarded Riff's blistered and scarred face. Okay this slob was tricky, but Moe had picked the right one. If he couldn't throw a scare into a man with a wife and baby, then no one could.

"I don't get it," Riff said. "How does this guy come into it?"

"He's writing a play," Kramer explained. "I happen to know the fellow who has rented him a ranch house. I've seen the place. I went there a couple of years ago. It's the most awful, lonely, Godforsaken spot you can imagine, but just the place for a guy who wants some peace and quiet to write a play. He's out there now with his wife, baby, a Vietnamese servant and an Alsatian dog." Kramer paused to stub out his cigar, then he pointed a thick finger at Riff. "Your first job is to fix the dog and the servant, then throw a hell of a scare into the Dermotts. Get it?"

"I can fix the dog," Riff said, looking searchingly at Kramer, "but how do you mean . . . fix the servant?"

"These Vietnamese can be tricky. You'll have all you want to do watching the Dermotts," Kramer said. "Keep the servant locked up in his quarters. He could make a bolt for it and make trouble."

Riff glanced at Chita who stared back at him with blank eyes. Impatiently, he shrugged.

"You'll put the telephone out of order and immobilize the cars," Kramer went on. "They have shotguns. Get them and put them out of the way. Make sure there are no other guns in the house. Then stick around until Moe arrives. You'll get down there around midnight the day before the snatch."

Riff got to his feet and crossed the room to the window. He looked through the curtains without touching them.

"What do we do about that jerk down there?" he asked.

"Not a thing. You two go down to the bar and buy yourselves a drink. Stick around for half an hour and then leave. That guy down there doesn't know you, but watch out you're not tailed. The chances are you won't be, but watch out. Moe leaves now. They know him and they'll tail him, but Moe's been tailed before. I'm checking out after lunch. They'll tail me." He showed his big, yellow teeth in a grin. "And I've been tailed before." He levered his bulk out of his chair and went over to a briefcase. From it he took a thick envelope which he tossed to Riff. "There's all the dope for you both. Maps, times and the whole setup. When you've got the stuff into your heads, burn it. We make the snatch tomorrow week. In the meantime, Moe will drop out of sight. On the day before the snatch, you will be at Twin Creek Tavern at five o'clock. Moe will be there. He'll give you final instructions and check to see you both know what you're to do. Got all that?"

Riff, who had been listening intently, nodded.

"How about some dough now?" he asked. "We're down to our last dollar."

"You'll find a hundred bucks in there," Kramer said,

waving to the envelope that Riff held in his hand. "That'll hold you. Moe will give you more when you meet. He'll also have a car for you." The small, hard eyes shifted to Chita. "Now, get down to the bar and remember if you foul this up, you'll have me as well as the Feds to reckon with!"

The Cranes went out, leaving Kramer and Moe together.

On Thursday night, Riff Crane drove on his motor-cycle from Pitt City towards Boston Creek. Some fifteen miles along the highway, he turned off on to a dirt road and drove a further fifteen miles until he arrived at the five-barred gate that guarded the entrance to Wastelands.

It was a warm, moonlit night. Riff pulled up outside the gate and sat for some moments peering up the long drive that he had been told by Moe led to the ranch house.

Riff was wearing his black leather uniform together with a pair of heavy goggles that half hid his face. He was sweating and uneasy. This was his first major job and he knew the consequences if the job turned sour.

He and Chita had talked and talked about the job during the past seven days. They were both mesmerized by the thought of laying their hands on ten thousand dollars, but at the same time, they both realized they would be risking their lives. This wasn't their usual small-time, petty thieving: this was suddenly big-time, and the pay-off, if the job turned sour, would be their finish. Both agreed after endless discussion that the gamble was justified. A character like Kramer, old as he was, wouldn't stick his neck out unless he was sure the job would work.

So Riff was now committed. In another nine hours, Chita would also be committed. Then there would be no turning back for either of them. The job had to succeed!

He opened the gate and wheeled his machine on to the grass verge. Moe had told him to walk the machine up to the house. Riff walked very cautiously, his eyes probing ahead. He had no stomach for a sudden encounter with an Alsatian dog. He had come provided with a lump of poisoned meat, but he knew if the dog saw him before it saw the meat, he would be the one to suffer.

It took him over an hour before he saw the ranch house in the moonlight, and by then sweat was streaming off him. He lowered his machine on to the grass and then moving rapidly, he approached the house.

He was lucky. He saw the dog before the dog either saw or smelt his approach. Riff dropped flat. The dog was standing up-wind, looking away into the darkness. It was some fifty yards from the ranch house and by the way the dog stood, its ears cocked forward, Riff guessed it sensed pending trouble.

He took the meat from the plastic bag and gauged the distance, then with a quick over-arm throw, he tossed the meat towards the dog. It was a good throw: the meat landed within a few feet of the dog. It whirled around, looking in Riff's direction, but Riff had already flattened in the sand, sure he would be invisible in his black uniform.

He lay there, sweating, his face buried in his arms, wondering if the dog was bounding towards him and knowing it would be fatal to make the slightest movement. He lay like that for a long, heart-thumping five minutes, then very slowly, he raised his head. He saw the black shape of the dog lying on its side. He stared, waited, then as there was no movement, he got slowly to his feet. He approached cautiously.

Ten minutes later, using a trenching tool he had brought with him, he had completed the burial of the dog. He spent some minutes smoothing down the sand, and then satisfied no one could tell where the dog was buried, he returned for his motor-cycle.

He wheeled the machine towards the outbuildings. Leaving it behind the garage, he paused to take stock of his surroundings.

Moe had supplied him with a detailed plan of the house and the outbuildings. He quickly identified the staff cabin. In the cabin would be the Vietnamese servant. He hesitated for a long moment whether to tackle the servant first or go to the house. He decided finally to go to the house. Moving like a long, black shadow, he silently circled the house. He quickly found the lead-in wires of the telephone. These he cut and rejoined with thin black string Moe had provided him with.

To the left of the house were french windows, leading to the gun-room. The lock on the door gave him little trouble and he moved silently into the big room. He had never before broken into a house and he was nervous. He stood in the darkness, moving the beam of a powerful flashlight around and listening. The beam came to rest on the gun-rack. He lifted the guns to the floor, then acting on Moe's instructions, he searched the drawers of the desk. He found the .38 automatic which he slid into his hip pocket. Then gathering up the guns, he walked out into the moon-light. When he was several hundred yards from the house he buried the guns in a sand dune.

All this took time. When he returned to the ranch house, it was a little after two o'clock. He closed the french win-dows, and with the aid of a paper-thin knife, he coaxed the catch to drop back into place.

He then walked quickly over to the garage. The door was unlocked. He swung it up, entered and lowered the door back in place. He turned on the electric light. Working quickly, he removed the sparking plugs from both cars. These he rolled up in his handkerchief. He carried them to the place where he had buried the guns and buried them too.

He was less nervous now. Everything was working out the way Moe had said it would. The dog was gone, the guns buried, the cars immobilized and the telephone fixed. He now had to take care of the Vietnamese servant.

From a long narrow pocket that ran the length of his left trouser leg, he drew out a bicycle chain. This was Riff's favourite weapon in a fight. Carefully he wound the chain like a bandage around his right fist. He flexed his fingers, making sure he hadn't the chain on too tightly, then satisfied, he headed for the staff cabin.

Di-Long was a shrimp of a man: fine boned, thin and nervy. A few minutes after two o'clock, he had woken out of an uneasy sleep. Usually, he slept through the night and to come awake so suddenly startled him. He lay for some moments in the dark, wondering what could have woken him, then he turned on the bedside light and got out of bed. He found he was thirsty and he went into the kitchen. He took a bottle of Coke from the refrigerator and snapped off the cap. With the bottle in his hand, he went to the cabin door, turned the key and pulled the door open. He moved out into the warm moonlight, looking across at the ranch house. As he stood there, Riff came silently around the side of the cabin.

The two men paused and looked at each other. The moonlight fell fully on Di-Long and Riff saw him clearly, whereas he was in the shadows and Di-Long only saw a towering black shadow that paralysed him with terror. The bottle of Coke slipped from his fingers and dropped silently into the sand. The spilt Coke made a black puddle as Riff, recovering first, his nerves tightening to vicious tension, moved forward. He saw Di-Long open his mouth. He knew that in a second the silent night air would be split by Di-Long's scream for help. His right fist, bound in its chain, swept up with the force of panic and with the speed of a striking snake.

Riff felt his fist crunch against the side of Di-Long's face. He felt the shock run up his arm. The Vietnamese catapulted back into the cabin and thudded to the floor. Only his thin ankles and small feet in their straw sandals remained in the pool of moonlight.

I shouldn't have hit him so hard, Riff thought, feeling a chill crawl up his spine. He knew he had hit the little man a terrible blow and he had a sickening idea that a man of that size couldn't recover from such a blow.

He looked over at the ranch house, feeling cold sweat running down his face.

My luck! he thought. What was he doing out here? Judas! He scared me! He was going to yell! I had to hit him! He unwound the chain and began to slide it back into his pocket when he became aware that the chain felt wet and sticky. Grimacing, he moved away from the shadow of the cabin and stared at the glistening dark patch that ran three-quarters of the length of the chain. He knew it was blood, and angrily, he scrubbed the chain clean in the sand. Satisfied that it was clean, he returned it to his pocket. Then he lit a cigarette, reached into his hip pocket and pulled out his flashlight. He stared at the small, narrow feet lying in the moonlight. Suppose he had killed this yellow punk? If he had, the job would blow up in his face. Kramer had said there was no risk as he had been certain he could talk the father of the kidnapped girl into paying up and keep the cops out of it, but if this little punk was dead, could Kramer keep the cops out?

Cursing under his breath, his heart thumping with panic, Riff pressed the button on the flashlight and threw the beam of light on to Di-Long's mangled and dead face.

CHAPTER FIVE

IF Zelda Van Wylie had been anything but the heiress to a billion dollars, it would be hard to say what she would have become: probably an inefficient saleswoman in some second-rate store or possibly an inaccurate copy-typist, but certainly with her education as it was and her indifferent intelligence, she couldn't have aspired to anything much higher.

But since she had the fortune to be born the only child of a Texas billionaire who was besotted with her, she was able to surmount to some extent the various handicaps with which nature had endowed her.

In appearance she was nothing to set a bonfire alight. This she had come to realize herself after hours of examining her naked body before a full-length mirror in her bathroom. She was pretty in a vapid, colourless way. She had large brown eyes that were generally sulky. She had a pretty nose and a nice mouth, but her chin faded away and this spoilt her overall appearance.

She was flat-chested and this distressed her as she admired those movie stars with over-developed busts. She was cursed with broad, matronly hips which she endeavoured to discipline by squeezing them in the most vicious girdles that the girdle market could provide. Her legs, however, were long and slender, and they were of great consolation to her.

From her birth she had been spoilt. Now at the age of eighteen years, she was bored, sexually frustrated, irritable and tiresome. She had enough intelligence to realize that the various young men who swarmed around her had a calculating eye on the riches that would eventually be hers. She had come to dislike and distrust men as a breed, but she worked off some of her sexual frustrations by poring over photographs in various Nature magazines of nude males with enormous muscles and bulging jock straps. Her other outlet was the adoration of certain male movie stars whom she pestered continually for their autographs and photographs. She considered men like Cary Grant, George Sanders and William Holden as the acme of male perfection.

In spite of having everything that money could buy, Zelda led a life of routine boredom. She went to the movies four times a week. The parties she arranged twice a week were vulgar and showy, but the young people who came were happy enough to eat the exotic food and drink the vast quantities of liquor provided, since most people become parasites whenever free food and drink are supplied. They sneered at her behind her back and offered nothing in return.

The few people whom she knew better than others thought it was sad that Zelda regarded her father as the reason for her unhappiness and boredom. If he hadn't had so much money, she was continuously saying, she would be happily married by now. Marriage was Zelda's idea of the cure for all her troubles and boredom. Her father's cloying affection smothered her like a blanket. His eager interest in everything she did or planned infuriated her. His constant suggestions to relieve her boredom were received with scorn. It was certainly due to his continual encouragement to have a good time with boys of her own age that soured Zelda's interest in men. John Van Wylie did his best for his daughter, but he failed to realize that by spoiling her, by showering everything on her she wanted or didn't want, he had become to her a nerve-tingling old bore.

On this summer morning in July, Zelda had risen at seven o'clock and had submitted to an hour's painful massage by an expert who lived in the enormous house for the express purpose of attempting to reduce Zelda's hip line. She then had a sulky breakfast with her father, and finally, a few minutes to nine o'clock, following her set routine, she left the house and got into the E-type Jaguar that waited for her at the bottom of the terrace steps.

She had decided to brighten her week-end by having her hair dyed the colour of fresh apricots. She had read in one of the numerous women's magazines that apricot was not only the latest colour for the hair, but it was also very *chic* and sophisticated. If there was anything that Zelda wished it was to be considered both *chic* and sophisticated.

She drove the Jag down the long drive. Among her very few talents, Zelda could handle any car like a racing expert.

At the far end of the drive, by the electrified gate, Chita waited. She stood beside a blue Ford Lincoln that Kramer had bought in some out-of-the-way car mart.

Some twenty yards from her, Moe Zegetti stood behind a thick clump of shrubs, aware that his heart was beating uneasily. He had no doubt that Chita would do what had been asked of her, but he knew, once they had the girl, there would be no turning back. Like Riff Crane, he too was aware that he was risking his life. Although trying to assure himself that Kramer had never made a mistake, he realized that Kramer was no longer the same man who had once ruled the Unions so ruthlessly and so successfully.

To add to his uneasiness, as he was leaving to meet Chita, he had had a telephone call from the hospital. The nurse had told him his mother was now very ill and was asking for him.

This was something Moe could do nothing about. He had committed himself to this job. He had told the nurse he would come as soon as he could. He knew his mother would understand.

His depressed thoughts were interrupted by the sound of an approaching car. He was in time to see the Jaguar as it swept up to the gate before he ducked out of sight.

By now Chita had lifted the hood of the car. She was wearing a blue and white cotton dress, bought with Kramer's money for this occasion and her dyed hair was tied neatly back with a piece of blue ribbon. She looked like any average American girl you see in their thousands.

Unlike Moe and her brother, Chita had entered into this affair with complete confidence. Already she was planning what they would do when they had the ten thousand dollars promised them. It never occurred to her, in spite of Riff's uneasiness, that the job could turn sour.   .

As Zelda got out of her car to open the gate, she stared enviously at Chita. She saw by the hard nipples pushing against the cheap material of Chita's dress that this girl wasn't wearing these wretchedly uncomfortable "falsies" that she was forced to wear.

"Can you help me?" Chita asked, her smile wide and friendly. "There's something wrong with the ignition. Is there a garage near here?"

Watching and listening, Moe nodded his head with approval. Chita was giving a natural and acceptable performance.

Zelda liked the look of this girl. She was from a world in which she never had the chance of mixing. The girl interested her.

"There's a garage along the highway. I'll take you there ... get in."

It was as easy as that.

As Chita slid into the car, she said, "Gee! What a beaut! Is it yours?"

Zelda nodded as she pressed the starter.

"Yes ... you like it?"

"I bet it does over a hundred."

This was the wrong thing to have said for Zelda was a show-off. With her foot gently squeezing the gas pedal, Zelda slid through the gears. The car surged forward, and within seconds the speedometer needle was flicking aound one hundred and thirty-five miles an hour.

Moe who was about to get into the Lincoln saw the Jag literally vanish from sight. Cursing, he started the Lincoln and swung out on to the highway.

Realizing that Moe couldn't possibly catch up with them at this speed, Chita put her hands to her face and screamed, "It's too fast! Please! It's too fast!"

Zelda laughed. She delighted in scaring anyone with speed. She slowed down until they were moving at a sedate seventy miles an hour.

"Did it really scare you? I often drive as fast as that . . . I adore speeding!"

"I thought I did," Chita said and looked over her shoulder through the rear window. There was no sign of Moe. "But . . . that was too fast!" She paused, then went on. "It's some car! You wouldn't be going to San Bernadino, would you? I have a date . . . I'm late already."

"That's where I am going," Zelda said, "but we can stop off at the garage and get them to fix your car. They can drive it to San Bernadino for you."

Chita could see the Shell sign ahead of them. Quickly she said, "It doesn't matter. I'll get a taxi back. I really want to get to S.B. as soon as I can. I'm late already."

Zelda shrugged and zipped the Jaguar past the service station. Then, glancing in the driving mirror, she exclaimed, "Oh hell! Not again!"

"What is it?" Chita asked sharply.

"A damn speed cop," Zelda said in disgust. "Sorry, but I'd better stop," and she slowed, pulled to the side of the road and stopped.

A moment later, a big, red-faced cop pulled up beside the car.

Chita sat motionless, her hands clenched tightly between her knees. She kept her face turned slightly away from the cop as he got off his motor-cycle and leaned into the car.

"'Morning, Miss Van Wylie," he said with a beaming smile. "You were clocking a hundred and thirty just now. Sorry, but I've got to book you."

"Oh the hell with you and your wife and your children!" Zelda snapped. "Go ahead and book me! I hope you fall off your lump of iron and break your neck!"

The cop laughed.

"Sure, Miss Van Wylie, but for Pete's sake relax with the gas on this highway." He scribbled on a pad and gave her a ticket. "Your Pa okay, Miss Van Wylie?"

"As if you care," Zelda said and made a face at him. "He'll hate you worse than he does already when he hears of this."

The cop laughed again. It gave him a kick to hand a

speeding ticket to one of the richest girls in the world. He knew Zelda well. He gave her a ticket at least once a week. His small, cop eyes shifted to Chita and they hardened. He stared for a long moment and Chita turned her head slowly and looked directly at him. For a brief moment, she felt suddenly small and naked under the probing, hard eyes, then forcing down this feeling of fear, she looked away.

The cop stepped back, giving an elaborate salute.

"Sorry to have stopped you, Miss Van Wylie, but you know how it is."

"Oh, go jump in the sea, Murphy," Zelda said and smiled. As she pulled once more on to the highway, Moe, in the Lincoln, came upon them. He kept going, driving past them, seeing the cop and feeling a clutch of fear at his heart.

Zelda said sharply, "That looks like your car."

They were now moving at a sedate forty miles an hour. Chita shook her head.

"My car? How could it be?"

Zelda looked puzzled, then she shrugged.

"I thought it looked like your car. What a bore about that cop! He'll follow me now all the way to S.B. I know him. He's a damned sadist. He loves booking me."

They were now climbing the hill to San Bernadino. Chita hesitated. She looked back. In the distance she could see the cop was following them: this could be dangerous. Maybe the cop would turn back once they reached the city. She opened her handbag and took out the flat flask Kramer had given her.

Zelda said, "What have you got there?"

With a sudden vicious note in her voice, Chita told her.

For several seconds Vic Dermott stared down at his blood-stained shoe, then with a little grimace of disgust, he flicked the shoe off his foot.

Carrie had sat down abruptly on the bed.

"It's blood, isn't it?" she asked in a tremulous voice.

"It could be . . . I don't know. Come on, Carrie, don't just sit there! Let's get going!"

The note of urgency in his voice forced Carrie to her feet.

"I'm nearly ready . . . Vic . . . it is blood, isn't it?"

Vic put on another pair of shoes. He was trying to remember where he could have picked up the blood that had stained his shoe. He was sure he would have noticed the blood if it had been out in the open. It must have been in the cabin, he told himself. Had Di-Long been hurt?

"Yes, I think so. Let's not talk about it now. Let's . . ." He stopped as he heard a sound that set him alert. It was the unmistakable sound of the door of the refrigerator closing.

"Did you hear that?" Carrie whispered, her eyes growing round. "There's someone in the kitchen!"

Vic hurriedly completed lacing his shoe, then he straightened. They looked at each other.

"Sounded like the refrig door shutting," he said, a little unnerved.

"It was! Oh, Vic! Someone's in the house!"

"All right . . . all right," Vic said. "Now don't get scared. You wait here. I'll go and see."

"No . . . you mustn't! Stay with me!"

"Darling . . . please . . ."

Moving silently, he went to the door of the bedroom which stood ajar. He listened, heard nothing, then looking over his shoulder, he said softly, "Stay with Junior," and then walked quickly and silently across the lobby to the kitchen door.

He paused in the doorway, his heart skipping a beat. The sight of Riff Crane in his shabby leather outfit and his scarred face, as he sat on the kitchen table gnawing at the leg of a chicken would have shaken men with much better nerves than Vic possessed.

Vic stood motionless, his heart now thumping and a cold wave of blood crawling up his spine.

Riff grinned at him.

"I bet I scared the crap out of you, Mac," he said. He

took a final bite out of the chicken leg and then flicked the bone across the kitchen.

As the bone skidded along the floor, Vic's fear turned to sudden anger.

"What do you think you're doing here?" he demanded. "Who are you?"

Riff eyed him. The fixed smile remained on his scarred face, but his eyes turned bleak and hard. He slid the bicycle chain from its pocket.

"Listen, Mac, you'll have to get used to me. I'm here for quite a while. Relax and you won't get pushed around. If you do what I tell you, you and the doll and the brat will be fine." He began to wind the chain slowly around his right fist. "I want coffee. Tell your doll to make me some ... hear me?"

"Get out of here!" Vic said. "Go on ... get out!"

Carrie came to the door. She caught her breath in a sharp gasp at the sight of Riff who eyed her and grinned.

"Nice," he said and leered. "Hi, baby-doll, get me some coffee or your pretty boy will get hurt."

Vic made a move forward, but Carrie, terrified at the sight of Riff, caught his arm.

"No, Vic! I'll give him coffee. Vic ... please!"

"That's the idea, baby. So long as you both do what you're told, no one gets hurt," Riff said. Then his expression changed to animal viciousness and he smashed his mailed fist down on the table. He yelled, "Coffee! Hear me? I won't tell you again!"

Vic caught hold of Carrie and pushed her roughly out of the kitchen.

"Stay with Junior," he said. "I'll handle this thug!"

As he turned he was in time to see Riff slide off the table and come at him with a sneering little grin on his face.

Vic had always kept himself fit and in his Varsity days he had been a pretty useful boxer, but he was no match for Riff who had been fighting brutally ever since he could remember. Vic shot out a left hand punch that Riff avoided by a lightning shift of his head, then his mailed fist slammed against the side of Vic's face and he went down as if struck by a sledge hammer. He lay unconscious at Riff's feet.

With a sharp scream, Carrie threw herself down on her hands and knees beside Vic, turning him and screaming again at the sight of the blood running down his face.

Riff unwound the chain and returned it to his pocket, then leaning forward, he twined his thick fingers in Carrie's hair and dragged her to her feet. She struck out blindly, but he gave her one paralysing shake that nearly broke her neck, then releasing her, he shoved her away.

"Coffee!" he bawled at her. "Hear me! Coffee or I'll put the boot to this jerk!"

Carrie steadied herself. She looked in horror at the steel-tipped ski-ing boots Riff was wearing, then not quite knowing what she was doing, she walked unsteadily across the kitchen and plugged in the percolator.

One of the telephones on Jay Dennison's desk buzzed urgently. He reached out and scooped up the receiver and growled, "Federal Field Office here. Inspector Dennison talking."

"Chief . . . this is Tom." Dennison recognized his future son-in-law's voice. "I'm sorry, but I've lost Kramer . . . just this minute. I guess he knew I was on his tail. I had Abe with me, but Kramer was too smart for both of us. He just dissolved into space."

Dennison's mouth tightened in anger. He was silent for a long moment while he bit back angry words that jumped to his tongue, then he said, "Well, okay, Tom: come back in and fast," and he hung up.

Ten minutes later the telephone buzzed again. This time it was Special Agent Harry Garson.

"Sorry, Chief, but we've lost Zegetti."

"I know," Dennison said savagely, "he just dissolved into space," and he slammed down the receiver. He leaned back in his chair and as he began to fill his pipe, the door opened and Tom Harper came in.

"Zegetti too," Dennison said. "So these two must be up to something . . . but what?"

Harper hooked a chair towards him and sat astride it.

"He was on to us, of course," he said, "but I didn't imagine he could pull such a vanishing trick. He went into the lobby of the . . ."

"Forget it," Dennison broke in impatiently. He got to his feet. "We're going for a ride." He slapped his hat on the back of his head and strode to the door. Twenty minutes later, he pulled up outside the long drive that led to Kramer's house.

"I bet he won't be home," he said, looking at the imposing wrought-iron gates, "but with any luck his wife will be. One time, she used to be a night club singer. I haven't seen her for years. From what I hear she's gone respectable. A visit from Federal Officers could scare her out of her girdle."

Tom got out of the car, opened the gates, then got back into the car.

"Sort of lives in style, doesn't he?" he said enviously as they drove through the park and towards the big house.

"So will you when you make your first million," Dennison said sourly. "He's made four."

A fat, pleasant-faced negress opened the front door.

"Mr. Kramer," Dennison said.

"Mr. Kramer ain't at home," the negress said, eyeing the two men with alert suspicion.

"Then Mrs. Kramer will do. Tell her it's Inspector Dennison, Federal Bureau." Dennison moved forward and the negress gave ground. The two men walked into the big, pleasantly furnished lobby.

Helene Kramer was coming down the broad stairs. She paused at the sight of these two men. Her hand went uneasily to her throat.

" 'Evening, Mrs. Kramer," Dennison said heavily. "We're Federal Officers. Mr. Kramer isn't in, I understand?"

Helene felt a cold sick emptiness form inside her. Federal Officers! Her hand tightened on the banister rail. This was a moment she had always been dreading since Jim had retired. She remained motionless, staring at the two men, panic in her eyes, then making an effort, she came down the stairs, waving Martha to the kitchen.

"Yes, Mr. Kramer is away," she said, trying to steady her voice. "What is it?"

"I wanted to see him. I'm Inspector Dennison." Dennison glanced at the open door leading into the lounge. "We can talk better in here," and he walked heavily into the big room, followed by Harper.

Helene hesitated, then followed them into the room.

"I don't understand . . . what is it?"

"I want to talk to him . . . it's police business. Where is he?"

Helene flinched. The two men watching her saw her hands turn into fists.

"New York. I – I don't know exactly where he is staying. He – he has gone up there on business."

Dennison stared for a long moment at her. He remembered the way she had looked fifteen years ago. She was rather faded now, he thought, and she was certainly in a panic.

"Isn't it a fact, Mrs. Kramer," he said in his cop voice, "that a man called Moe Zegetti, an ex-convict and a known criminal, visited this house a couple of weeks ago?"

Helene walked to a chair and sat down.

"Yes, he did. He is an old friend of my husband's. He was looking for a site to open a restaurant in Paradise City," she said slowly. "As he happened to be passing through, my husband naturally invited him to lunch. They have been friends for years."

Dennison rubbed the side of his face, an inquiring, sarcastic expression jumping into his eyes.

"Zegetti starting a restaurant? Did he tell you that?"

"Yes, that's what he told us," Helene said.

"Would it surprise you to know that Zegetti has been a third-rate waiter in a fifth-rate restaurant for the past months and he hasn't a dime to call his own?"

Helene closed her eyes, shivered and then looked anxiously at Dennison.

"I know nothing about the man," she said. "Only what he told my husband."

"Look, Mrs. Kramer," Dennison said, "we have nothing against either you or your husband. Your husband was one of the top racketeers in the business. He had the sense to pull out before we caught up with him. I have an idea he is coming out of retirement. I hope for your sake and his, he isn't. I hope for my sake he is. If you contact him, tell him I'm on to him. Tell him if he is starting something, he is heading for trouble. This is a friendly warning: you won't get another. Understand?" He jerked his head at Harper. "Come on, let's get out of here."

When the two men had driven away, Helene put her hands to her face and burst into tears.

While Inspector Dennison had been talking to Helene, Jim Kramer arrived by taxi at the Lake Arrowhead Hotel, a plush, de luxe hotel which, at this time of year, was crowded with rich visitors.

He signed the register in the name of Ernest Bendix. The previous week he had taken the precaution to telephone for a reservation and he was shown immediately to a comfortable suite with a balcony overlooking the lake.

He was feeling pleased with himself. The way he had shaken off those two Feds proved to him that he hadn't lost his touch. He hoped Moe had been as successful. After unpacking his bag, he went out on to the balcony. He sat there, admiring the view and smoking a cigar until a little after seven o'clock, then he went into the sitting-room and put through a call to Twin Creek Tavern. He asked to be connected with Mr. Marion: the name under which Moe had registered.

The two men talked briefly. Anyone chancing to listen-in would have gained no information from their conversation, but Kramer gathered all was well and the Cranes had arrived.

"Call me tomorrow when you have the safe delivery of the package," he said and hung up.

He wondered if he should call Helene, but decided against

it. He had told her he had urgent business in New York concerning Solly Lucas's death and for her not to worry if she didn't hear from him for a few days. He was a little uneasy at Helene's look of worry when he left. He knew she was no fool, and it irritated him to realize that she probably didn't believe his story. It would be dangerous to call her, he decided. She might easily have his call traced, and then she would know he wasn't in New York.

He had an excellent dinner served in his room and he spent the evening on the balcony, smoking and drinking whisky and listening to the crowd milling around on the terrace below.

He remained in his room during the following morning. A little after eleven o'clock, Moe telephoned. He sounded short of breath and there was a quaver in his voice that Kramer didn't like.

"We have the package," Moe said, "but there are complications."

"Where are you?" Kramer demanded, an edge to his voice.

"At Lone Pine. I'm calling from a booth."

In the hotel lobby there were a number of telephone booths that Kramer knew didn't go through the hotel switchboard.

"Stay right where you are. Give me your number. I'll call you back," he said.

This he knew to be dangerous. One of the switchboard operators might be listening in, but he had to know what the complications were.

Moe gave him the number and hung up.

Kramer took the elevator down to the crowded lobby of the hotel. He was lucky to find a telephone booth unoccupied. Shutting himself in, he called the number Moe had given him. Moe answered immediately.

"What is it?" Kramer demanded. "What's gone wrong?"

Moe told him about the speed cop.

"If the job turns sour," Moe said uneasily, "the cop will

have a description of Chita. He got a good look at her. It was bad luck, but this girl drove like a lunatic."

Kramer thought quickly.

"It won't turn sour," he said. "That's the trick of this thing. The cops won't come into it. Relax. How's the Van Wylie girl behaving?"

"Chita is handling her . . . no trouble there. The acid scared the hell out of her. I thought you should know about the cop."

"Yeah. Okay, Moe, you get off. You'll be at Wastelands in another hour. I'll call you there at twelve-thirty. Crane was told to put the line out of order. Get it going again as soon as you arrive. When I know you've got there, I'll talk to Van Wylie."

Moe said he understood and he hung up.

Kramer returned to his suite and went out on to the balcony. One never knew for certain with any job, he thought uneasily. The speed cop disturbed him. If he was one of those who stuck his nose in other people's business, he might just possibly report to headquarters that the Van Wylie girl was travelling with a girl out of her class. The chances were he wouldn't, but he might.

Slightly less sure of himself, Kramer tried to relax in the sunshine. He found he was continually looking at his watch. Finally, a few minutes to half past twelve, he went down to the lobby and put a call through to Wastelands.

There was some delay, then the operator said, "I'm sorry, but the line is out of order. Our engineer is on his way out there now. If you will make your call again in about an hour, I should be able to connect you."

His face suddenly like granite, Kramer thanked her and hung up.

Now things weren't going his way. It was possible the hairdresser might call Van Wylie to tell him his daughter hadn't kept her appointment. Van Wylie might wait until lunch-time and then inquire at the Country Club, knowing his daughter always lunched there after her hairdressing appointment. When they reported not seeing her, the chances were he would call the police and then the fat would be in the fire.

Our engineer is on his way out there.

Would Moe be able to handle the situation? What would the engineer think when he found the telephone lines cut? Would he report back? Would his report go to the police? Everything now depended on how Moe handled it. Kramer suddenly became aware that his collar was too tight. He dug two thick fingers down the collar-band and eased it. His mind worked swiftly. He would have to assume that Moe and Chita had got the Van Wylie girl to Wastelands. He had to call Van Wylie before Van Wylie alerted the police.

He took from his pocket a small notebook. In it, among many other telephone numbers, he had noted down Van Wylie's number.

As he began to dial the number, he suddenly hesitated and cut the connection. He had very nearly made a mistake! A man like Van Wylie would draw a lot of water in this district. He could very easily get this call traced to the hotel and that could be fatal if there were an investigation.

Leaving the booth, Kramer hurried out into the hot sunshine. He flagged a taxi and told the driver to take him to Main Street. a few minutes later, he was in the General Post Office and dialling Van Wylie's number.

A man said, "Mr. Van Wylie's residence."

"I want to talk to Mr. Van Wylie," Kramer said. "It's urgent ... to do with Miss Van Wylie."

"What is the name, please?"

"He won't know me. I am a friend of his daughter. Mannikin's my name."

"Will you hold on for a moment, please?"

John Van Wylie had just returned from his routine morning ride. He was in his study, a double Martini on his desk and he was flicking through a big pile of mail.

Fellows, his manservant, knocked and came in. He told Van Wylie that a Mr. Mannikin was on the telephone.

"He says, sir, he is a friend of Miss Zelda's."

John Van Wylie was a short, heavily-built man with a

broad flat face, small hard eyes with fleshy bags, a large thin mouth and a square aggressive jaw. He looked what he was: the son of a wagon driver and a man who could turn one dollar into ten and care little how he did it.

He looked for a long moment at Fellows, his eyes becoming slits. Not once could he remember any friend of Zelda's calling him up. He moved to the telephone and with his left hand, he switched on a tape recorder hooked up with the telephone and with his right hand he picked up the receiver.

"Yes?"

"Mr. Van Wylie?"

"Yes."

"This is to do with your daughter. You have no reason to be alarmed . . . yet," Kramer said, speaking quickly, not certain if Van Wylie had some means of getting the call traced. "Your daughter has been kidnapped. She is perfectly safe and will be returned to you within a few days unharmed. However, if you attempt to go to the police or do anything you're not told to do, then you won't see the girl again. We are a big organization and your house is being watched: your telephone line has been tapped. Do nothing, say nothing and wait. You'll be hearing from me again tomorrow. Again I warn you if you want to see your daughter again, wait and do nothing." He cut the connection and leaving the booth, he walked quickly over to the taxi rank and told one of the drivers to take him back to the hotel.

John Van Wylie stood for a long moment motionless, the telephone receiver clenched in his big, powerful hand. His face had lost a little of its colour, but his mouth was suddenly an ugly, cruel line. He replaced the receiver and turned off the tape recorder.

"Get Andrews," he said in a curt, hard voice.

Fellows went quickly away. A couple of minutes later, Merrill Andrews, Van Wylie's secretary, a tall, bronze, hard-bitten Texan wearing a sports shirt and blue jeans, came into the room. Van Wylie was talking to the telephone supervisor.

"The call was made from the General Post Office, Mr. Van Wylie," she said in a flutter to be talking to one of the richest men in the world. "One of the public booths."

Van Wylie thanked her and hung up. He turned to Andrews who was looking at him expectantly.

"A call has just come through saying Zelda's been kidnapped," Van Wylie said. "Get the hairdresser's and the Country Club. Find out if Zelda's been there."

Andrews stepped to the telephone as Van Wylie walked to the window. Van Wylie stared out, his hands gripped behind his back. Andrews talked quickly and efficiently. After a few minutes, he said, "Miss Zelda didn't arrive at the hairdresser's. She hasn't been seen at the club. Shall I call the Federal Agents?"

"No," Van Wylie said, a snarl in his voice. "Say nothing to anyone about this! Now, get out! I have some thinking to do!"

CHAPTER SIX

RIFF stood on the veranda of Wastelands, a cigarette dangling from his thick lips. He watched the approaching car as it came up the long winding drive and he fingered the butt of Dermott's automatic that he had thrust into the hip pocket of his leather trousers.

It was a few minutes past noon. Riff had locked the Dermotts and their baby in the front room. The windows were open, but there was no other exit. From where he stood he could see the windows and he had no worry that they could escape. By hitting the man so hard, he had knocked the guts out of him and also out of his wife.

But Riff was savagely uneasy. He had killed the Vietnamese. This, he told himself, was the result of moving too fast from small-time into big-time. He cursed himself for hitting the little man so hard. A man of Dermott's build could take a crushing blow, but a shrimp like the yellow-skin just couldn't. Well, it was done now. Riff had decided to say nothing to Moe about the Vietnamese. He had come to realize during his short association with Moe that clever as this Wop was supposed to be, he was soft. If he knew Riff had killed the Vietnamese, he was likely to flip his lid.

The car pulled up a few yards from him. Moe was driving. Chita and the kidnapped girl sat at the back.

Riff looked curiously at the girl, letting smoke drift down his thick nostrils. He was disappointed. He had hoped for something more glamorous, but when she got out of the car, he saw her broad hips and his eyes narrowed. Maybe she mightn't be so bad after all, he thought, as he walked down the veranda steps, deliberately exaggerating his rolling swagger.

"Okay?" Moe asked anxiously as he got out of the car.

Riff raised a dirty thumb.

"Nothing to it . . . and you?"

"Yeah." Moe paused, then looked at the car. "I had better get it under cover. Where's the garage?"

Riff pointed.

"Lots of room in there."

Moe got into the car and drove it over to the garage. Riff looked at Chita who was standing beside Zelda. He lifted his eyebrows and she nodded. He then looked at Zelda who was eyeing him curiously. She had got over her scare now and was relaxed. From what Moe had told her, she hadn't anything to worry about. It was just a matter of how long it would take her father to pay out the ransom.

This dirty-looking man in the shabby black leather uniform with his scarred face intrigued her. He was the kind of thug she so often saw on the movies: the type who sent hot blood through her body and gave her erotic dreams.

Riff saw the hot flush that stained her face and the way her eyes darkened. He knew he had set off a spark in her.

He leered at her.

"I'm Riff," he said. "What's your name, baby?"

"Zelda Van Wylie," Zelda said. Her flush began to recede. For her age, she was pretty self-possessed. This could be fun, she was thinking. God! What a hunk of a man! If only he were a bit cleaner! Those shoulders! Those brutal hands! "You in this too?"

"Sure, baby," Riff said, eyeing her over. "We're all in it. Come on in and make yourself at home." He took three swaggering steps forward and put his hand possessively on her arm. Now he was close to her, she could smell his dirt and see the grime on his neck, his black fingernails and the dust in his close-cropped hair.

She jerked away from him, her nose wrinkling in disgust.

"Don't touch me!" she said sharply. "Keep away from me! You – you smell!"

Riff stood very still. The muscles of his face moved under his grey-white skin like the ripple of moving water. His eyes narrowed and his mouth turned into a white, thin line.

Recognizing the signs, Chita said, "Cut it out, Riff! Hear me? Stop it!"

The sudden vicious fury that now burned in the narrow eyes shocked Zelda who backed away.

Chita exclaimed. "Riff! Cut it out! He's coming!"

"Okay, baby," Riff said softly, staring at Zelda. "I'll remember. Plenty of time . . . I'll remember."

Moe came up, wiping his sweating face with a soiled handkerchief.

"What are you doing out here?" he demanded. "Get her inside!"

Chita nodded to Zelda and the two girls walked up the steps and into the house.

Riff stared after them. His eyes moved down the length of Zelda's back.

"What's happened to the Dermotts?" Moe asked.

Riff said nothing until the girls were out of sight, then he turned and stared at Moe.

"Got 'em locked up in the front room. The guy got a little frisky and I had to tap him. They won't trouble us now."

"The dog?"

"Nothing to it. I've buried it."

"The servant?"

Riff jerked his thumb towards the staff cabin.

"He's locked in there. I scared the crap out of him. No trouble with him now. He can't get out."

"You'd better repair the telephone line," Moe said. "The boss will be coming through any time now."

Riff resented taking orders from anyone. He eyed Moe and then shrugged his heavy shoulders.

"Can't be done," he said. "I cut 'em, but there's no slack to fix 'em with."

"Look in the garage," Moe said impatiently. "There may be some spare wire there. We've got to get the line repaired. Get going!" And he walked up the steps and into the house.

Riff picked his nose thoughtfully. It was a little too soon

for a showdown. Shrugging, he walked with lazy strides towards the garage.

Vic Dermott, lying on the settee in his study, heard the car pull up. His head ached violently and he had extensive bruising down the right side of his face. He had been conscious for over three hours, but he was only now slowly recovering. Carrie sat by his side, holding his hand, anxiously watching him. They hadn't said much to each other. The blow had been so violent, Vic felt his brain had come adrift, but at the sound of the car, he attempted to sit up.

"Stay still," Carrie said, getting to her feet. She looked through the window to see Zelda and Chita confronting Riff. Then she saw Moe drive the car over to the garage. "There are three more of them. Oh, Vic! What is happening? Who are these people?"

Gritting his teeth, Vic slowly sat up. For a moment the room spun around before his eyes, then everything came into sharp focus. He looked beyond Carrie through the open window.

Riff was talking to Zelda. Vic looked at the girl, then at Chita before his eyes flicked back to Zelda.

"It can't be," he muttered and passed his hand before his eyes, then stared again. Zelda and Chita were now walking towards the house. "That girl . . . it can't be." They were out of sight now and they could be heard moving through the lounge. "She looks exactly like that Van Wylie girl." Vic touched the side of his face and winced. "You know . . . she's supposed to be one of the richest girls in the world. Zelda . . . isn't that her name?"

Carrie said breathlessly, "Of course! I knew I had seen her somewhere before." She looked at Vic. "They've kidnapped her!"

"Could be and they are using this place as a hide-out." He reached for a sponge lying in a bowl of ice-water, wrung it out and held it to his face. "Could be," he went on. "It's a damn smart idea. Who would think of looking for them here?"

"There's a car coming!" Carrie exclaimed. She pointed out of the window. Some miles down the dirt road they could see a cloud of dust that always heralded an approaching car.

Vic relaxed back on the cushion. His head began to ache so violently that he suddenly didn't care any more. Then Junior began to whimper and Carrie hurried over to him.

Carrie hadn't been the only one to have seen the approaching car.

Riff came quickly into the lounge where Zelda and Chita were sitting. Moe was making himself a drink at the cocktail bar.

"Car coming!" Riff said. "Be here in five minutes!"

Moe hurriedly set down his glass and went to the window. He stared at the approaching cloud of dust and his fingers nervously touched the butt of a .38 he had in a holster under his coat. His brain worked quickly. He turned to Chita. "You act the maid," he said. "If they come here, go to the door and say the Dermotts are out. If there's trouble, we're right behind you." He looked at Zelda. "You make a sound and you'll be sorry."

Riff grinned.

"She won't. Will you, baby?" he said, staring at Zelda.

She stared back at him and then looked away, her expression contemptuous.

"You're cute," Riff sneered. "Baby, there's a time coming for you. I'm . . ."

"Shut up!" Moe barked. "Watch the Dermotts! Keep them quiet. I'll stay here."

Riff eyed him, broadened his sneering grin and went across the lobby, unlocked the study door and went in.

Chita, who was looking out of the window, said, "It's a telephone repair truck."

Moe cursed under his breath.

"They're checking the line. When they see it's cut . . ."

"Oh, cool off!" Chita said sharply. "I'll fix them."

As the truck with a ladder on its roof and two young engineers in the cab pulled up outside the house, Chita crossed the lobby and opened the front door.

The doorman of the Lake Arrowhead Hotel touched his cap as Kramer came across the crowded lobby.

"Your car's ready, sir," he said. "It was only for two days, wasn't it?"

"Yeah," Kramer said and slipped a five-dollar bill into the doorman's expectant hand. "If I need it for longer, I'll let you know."

The porter conducted him to a Buick convertible that stood in one of the hotel's parking bays and opened the door.

"Get you a car any time you want, sir," he said as Kramer settled himself behind the driving wheel.

Kramer nodded to the doorman, engaged gear and headed for Pitt City.

Some minutes after three o'clock, in the blazing heat of the afternoon sun, Kramer drove up the dirt road leading to Wastelands. He pulled up at the gate, got out, opened the gate, drove the car forward, got out and shut the gate.

The heat made him sweat and he was aware that the nagging pain in his left side had returned. As he drove up the winding road that led directly to the house, he felt a sudden loss of confidence. He was getting old, he told himself. If something should go wrong! If, after all those years in the rackets, he should suddenly find himself in a police cell! The pain in his side increased, and he put a big, fleshy hand to his chest. But there was no turning back now. He trusted Moe. The plan was right. It couldn't turn sour.

When he pulled up outside the front door of Wastelands, he saw Riff lounging in a bamboo chair, his feet on the veranda rail. Riff stood up as Kramer got out of the car.

Kramer said briskly, "Get this car out of sight. Where's Moe?"

Riff stared at him, his narrow eyes probing. He jerked his thumb towards the front door and with a lazy movement, vaulted the veranda rail, got in the car and drove it towards the garage.

As Kramer came up the steps, the front door opened and Moe came out into the hot sunshine.

The two men paused and looked at each other.

"Well?" Kramer demanded, a snap in his voice.

"It's okay," Moe said. "The girl's here. There's been no trouble with the Dermotts. We had a telephone engineer out here because Riff cut the lines, but Chita handled him. He went away satisfied. We're in the clear."

Kramer drew in a long, slow breath. He showed his discoloured teeth in a sudden, wide grin of relief.

"When you want something well planned you come to me, huh?" He moved into the house. "Where's Dermott? He's the guy I want to talk to."

Moe motioned him to the study door.

"He's in there with his wife." As Kramer began to move forward, Moe said, "Jim . . . just a moment. He got a little out of hand. Riff had to hit him."

Kramer stopped in his tracks. His fleshy face turned a dusty red as he turned to glare at Moe.

"Hit him? What the hell do you mean?"

Moe shifted uneasily.

"Well, the guy tried to be a hero. Riff had to quieten him."

Kramer removed his Stetson hat and wiped his sweating head.

"How bad is he?"

"He's okay now, but Riff hits hard."

Kramer grunted, then went to the study door, turned the handle and walked into the big, airy room.

Vic and Carrie were seated side by side on the settee. At the sight of this big, elderly man, Vic got slowly to his feet.

"I have to apologize, Mr. Dermott," Kramer said in his hearty, insincere business voice. "I hear one of my boys got a little excited." He stared at the livid bruise that extended down the side of Vic's face. "I'm sorry."

"Who are you?" Vic said. "Just what are all these — these thugs doing in my house?"

Kramer moved further into the room and sat down. He nodded to Carrie who was staring at him.

"My respects, Mrs. Dermott. Sorry for all this, but it is unavoidable." He looked at Vic. "Mr. Dermott, it is your misfortune to have rented this place. I hope you will be co-operative. If you'll sit down, I'll tell you exactly what it is all about and then you can decide for yourself whether or not you want to play along with me."

Vic and Carrie exchanged glances, then controlling his anger, Vic sat down. He reached for a cigarette, lit it as he eyed the big, red-faced man.

"Go ahead," he said. "I'm in need of an explanation."

"I've been lucky enough to have kidnapped one of the richest girls in the world," Kramer said, his face splitting into a wide grin. "I reckon she is worth four million dollars to her father. This place struck me as the ideal head-quarters to negotiate the ransom and an excellent place in which to hide the girl. I am being as brief as I can, Mr. Dermott. I have picked on you to talk to the girl's father and to convince him to pay up without a fuss. You will also collect the money and bring it to me."

Vic stiffened. He began to say something but stopped as he saw Kramer's evil little eyes staring fixedly at Carrie.

After a pause, Kramer went on, "I understand you have a baby . . . a boy?" He looked across the room where Junior was sleeping. "I like babies. The last thing I want is for kids to run into trouble. Know what I mean?"

Carrie put her hand on Vic's. Her skin felt hot and dry.

"I think so . . . if I don't do what you want," Vic said evenly, "you'll take it out of the baby . . . that's it, isn't it?"

Kramer smiled expansively.

"I like dealing with a man like you, Mr. Dermott. You're quick, intelligent and reasonable. This fellow, Riff . . . he's dangerous, and he's a little out of my control. I'm afraid he pushed you around." There was a threatening pause, then Kramer went on, "He doesn't give a damn who he pushes around: a man, a woman or even a baby."

Vic thought of Riff. He was one of those morons spewed up from the gutter capable of anything. All he was now concerned about was to keep Carrie and Junior safe.

"If I think I can persuade Van Wylie to pay up, I'll try," he said evenly.

Kramer's eyes narrowed.

"Who said anything about Van Wylie?" There was a dangerous snarl in his voice.

"I recognized the girl," Vic said impatiently. "She's a well-known personality. What do you want me to do?"

"No, Vic!" Carrie said. "You . . ."

Vic shook his head at her. The expression in his steady eyes brought her to abrupt silence. He turned once more to Kramer who was easing his bulk in his chair.

"You won't have any trouble," Kramer said. "All you have to do is to talk to Van Wylie and convince him that if he doesn't pay up, he's not seeing his daughter again. I have an idea he'll be pretty easy to convince. I want him to give you ten certified cheques for four hundred thousand dollars each. Signed by a man of Van Wylie's financial weight there'll be no difficulty in cashing cheques for that amount. It will be your job, Mr. Dermott, to go to various banks and cash these cheques. I'll give you a list of the banks: they are well spread out and you will have no trouble. Then you will hand the money to me. I will immediately release Miss Van Wylie and you will be free to get on with your play." He grinned. "Not very difficult, is it?"

"I suppose not," Vic said quietly.

Kramer stared for a long moment at him, his face a sudden ugly, hard mask.

"If you fail to convince Van Wylie that he must pay up, that he is not to bring the police into this, that he will never see his daughter again if he tries anything smart, then your wife and baby will land in real trouble. I want you to understand this. The money is important to me. I need it. I am in a position that does not allow for any sentiment. I assure you if things go wrong whether through your fault or Van Wylie's obstinacy, the first persons to suffer will be your wife and baby." Kramer leaned forward, his eyes bloodshot and cold. "I want you to imagine what a slob like Riff would do to a baby. He likes handling someone who can't hit back. You are a man of imagination. You should know what I am driving at. I assure you if we fall down on this plan, I will simply withdraw and leave you all to Riff. So be very careful, Mr. Dermott. Understand?" He got to his feet. "I'll leave you two to talk it over. Tomorrow morning I expect you to see Van Wylie. It will take you three days to collect the money. Then you will return here. If all goes well, you won't see us again. If there is trouble . . ." He shrugged his shoulders and started to the door.

Vic said, "Wait. What's happened to my servant?"

Kramer paused, his hand on the door handle.

"Nothing's happened to him. He's all right."

"I don't believe it," Vic said, getting to his feet. "There's blood in his sleeping quarters . . . he's disappeared."

Kramer's face hardened. He opened the door.

"Riff!" His deep, heavy voice resounded through the ranch house.

There was a moment's delay, then Riff lounged into the lobby. He eyed Kramer.

"You want me?"

"The Vietnamese? What's happened to him?" Kramer demanded.

Riff jerked his thumb towards the staff cabin.

"He's in there," he said.

"He's lying!" Vic exclaimed. "He is not there!"

Riff grinned evilly at him.

"You want another poke in your puss, palsy?"

"Belt up!" Kramer snapped. He went out of the room. After staring at Vic for a long moment, Riff followed him. Out in the lobby, Kramer said, "What happened to the yellow-skin?"

"He got excited," Riff said casually. "I had to give him a little poke. He bled a bit, but he's okay now."

Kramer grunted. He had too much on his mind to worry about a Vietnamese servant.

Moe came from the living-room and Kramer beckoned to him.

"I'll stay the night. There's room for me, isn't there?"

"Sure," Moe said. "There's plenty of room."

"Where's the Van Wylie girl?"

"Chita's taking care of her."

"No chance of her getting away?"

"It's a fifteen-mile walk to the highway. No chance at all. This is the perfect setup."

As the two men walked into the living-room, still talking, Riff wandered out onto the veranda and sat down. He stared bleakly at the spot, some hundred yards from where he was sitting, where he had buried Di-Long.

It was not until after midnight that the Cranes got together alone for the first time since the kidnapping.

Riff was sitting in the bamboo lounging chair at the far end of the veranda where he could watch all the windows of the rooms where the Dermotts and Zelda were sleeping.

Chita came out of the shadows and joined him. She sat on the floor at his feet and took the cigarette he handed to her.

"What's biting you?" she asked as she moved her head forward to light the cigarette from the match flame he had struck alight. "That girl?"

Riff moved uneasily. It always irritated him that Chita could probe into his most secret thoughts. He made a sneering grimace.

"Think she worries me?"

"Yes . . . I think she might."

"Screw it! No skirt has ever worried me."

There was a long silence while they both smoked. Knowing something was wrong, Chita waited. Her brother always got around to his troubles in his own time. She never attempted to rush him. But after some ten minutes had gone by in silence, she said, "Well, I guess I'll turn in. Zegetti's relieving you, isn't he?"

"Yeah." Riff hesitated then as Chita began to move, he went on, "That yellow-skin . . ."

Here it comes, Chita thought, as she sank back on the veranda floor.

"Shouldn't we give him something to eat?" she said. "I've forgotten about him. He must be hungry."

"Think so? I don't." Riff eased the neckband of his shirt with a dirty finger. "He's dead."

Chita drew in a quick startled breath. She remained

very still, staring at her brother who scowled at the burning end of his cigarette. He flicked the butt over the veranda rail and immediately lit another.

"Dead? What happened?"

"He was going to yell. He took me by surprise. I tapped him too hard," Riff said, scowling. "I had the chain on. His goddam face busted like a dropped egg."

Chita wiped her sweating hands on the skirt of her dress. Her quick, animal intelligence told her at once that now they were in real trouble.

Steadying her voice, she said, "What have you done with him?"

"Buried him out there." Riff pointed to the sand dunes.

"If they ever find out he's dead," Chita said slowly, "Kramer won't be able to keep the cops out of this."

"Think I'm dumb?" Riff snarled. "I've thought of that. I tell you it wasn't my fault! I just hit him too hard."

For a long moment, Chita fought against a rising panic, Kidnapping! Now murder!

"You'll have to take food to the cabin every day," she said finally. "Suppose you tell Zegetti that the yellow-skin had seen you, but there's no need for him to see him or me. The less faces he sees the safer for us all. Zegetti will fall for that line. That'll give us a couple of days to see how it works out."

Riff thought about this. It made sense to him and he nodded.

"But I don't see how we fix it in the end," he said. "The punk's dead and I killed him."

"I'll think about it," Chita said. "Could be we could push the killing on to Zegetti. The cops know him. They don't know us."

"Oh, wrap up!" Riff snarled. "They'll know when he sparked out. Moe wasn't here until fifteen hours after I hit the punk. These cops are smart."

"I'll think about it," Chita said again. She paused, then, "Riff . . . leave that girl alone."

Riff stared at her, his narrow eyes glittering.

"I'm fixing her good," he said viciously. "No — talks

that way to me! You keep out of it! I'm going to fix her
and I'll fix her good!"

Chita got to her feet.

"You touch her and you'll be sorry," she said. "You want
to use your head. We're in bad trouble enough now, but if
you interfere with her, we'll be up to the neck in it. Can't
you see . . . we're in real trouble already?" It was typical of
the Cranes to share the responsibility of each other's mis-
takes. "Get your mind off her. What is she anyway? All she
has is a fat behind . . . nothing else. You start thinking about
the yellow-skin. I want to leave here with ten thousand
dollars which I can spend!"

She went away, leaving Riff scowling out across the moonlit desert.

Vic and Carrie lay side by side in one of the single beds
in their bedroom. Carrie wanted to be as close as she could
get to her husband. The cot in which Junior slept peacefully
had been moved to within arm's reach of the bed.

Neither of them had been able to sleep. Carrie began
again on the subject they had already discussed and discussed.

"You can't do it, Vic," she said. "You can't act as this
man's go-between. You can surely see that, can't you?"

Vic moved impatiently.

"I don't give a damn about the Van Wylies," he said,
pulling her close to him. "I have to do it for our sakes. He
wasn't bluffing. Carrie . . . I'm pretty sure Di-Long's
dead."

Carrie stiffened.

"Oh, no!"

"Well, if he isn't dead, then he's badly hurt. I picked that
blood up on my shoe in his cabin. That thug hits!" He
touched his aching face. "If he hit Di-Long . . ."

"Don't Vic!"

"These people mean business. I don't know who the fat
man is, but you can see for yourself, he is just as big a thug
as the young one. If I don't do what he says, he could take it
out of you and Junior. He's not bluffing. I have to do it."

"But, Vic, you aren't going to leave me alone with them?" Carrie said, her voice jumping a note.

"They aren't looking for trouble," Vic said quietly. "They only want the money. They won't harm you . . . unless I fail to get the money for them. I'm sure of that."

"I wish I was as sure. You really mean you're going off tomorrow and leave me with these awful people?"

Vic drew in a long, slow breath.

"Unless you have another suggestion, Carrie, that's what I have to do."

"Suggestion? What do you mean?"

"What else do you want me to do?"

"I keep telling you! Stay here with Junior and me of course!"

"You want me to tell that man I won't do what he asks?" Vic said quietly.

They were back where they had started. They had gone over this again and again. Vic understood how Carrie felt to be left alone with these thugs, but he realized that if she and Junior were to remain safe there was no other alternative.

"I have to go, darling," he said.

Carrie closed her eyes. She clung closer to him, fighting back the tears that tried to escape through her tightly closed eyelids.

Moe Zegetti lay in the comfortable bed in the fourth guest-room. Although he hadn't been so comfortable in years, his mind was uneasy. He was thinking of his mother. It was now two weeks since he had seen her. He had had no news of her since he had left 'Frisco. He knew she was pretty bad, but he had great faith in her toughness. When this job was over, he would be worth a quarter of a million dollars! Big Jim had said so and when Big Jim made a promise, he stuck to it. With that kind of money, Moe told himself, no matter how bad his mother was, he would be able to fix anything for her.

But he hadn't the money as yet. He worried about the speed cop. He worried too about Riff Crane. That boy was bad . . . really bad. Moe didn't like the way he had looked at the Van Wylie girl. There was trouble ahead with those two: he was sure of that. And Riff had Dermott's gun. That was bad. A punk like Riff with his kind of nature should never have a gun.

In the room next to Moe's, Zelda lay awake. She wondered what her father was doing right at this very moment. She moved her long legs under the sheet and smiled into the moonlit shadows. He must be laying square eggs, she thought. She had no doubt he would pay up and pay up fast. Really it was a pity that it would be over so soon for she was frankly enjoying herself. The first moment of shock when that girl had squirted acid on the Jag door and she had seen the way the leather had just peeled away had terrified her, but once she was over the shock and she realized she was in no danger, this affair had begun to amuse and excite her. After all, she was in luxury. No one could complain about the room in which she was. Then there was this man with the scarred face. Zelda felt a hot rush of blood through her at the thought of him. He was an animal, but what an animal!

Her hands went under the sheet and she closed her eyes. The image of Riff filled her mind. She began to breathe unevenly and heavily: soon she was panting, her legs tightly pressed together. Later still, she fell asleep.

CHAPTER SEVEN

KRAMER sat in a lounging chair, a cigar gripped between his teeth. Behind him stood Moe Zegetti. Opposite him, in another lounging chair, sat Vic Dermott.

From where he sat, Vic could see through the window across the patio to the garage. The garage doors were open. Riff was working on Vic's Cadillac. He had already replaced the sparking plugs. He was now removing the licence plates and replacing them with plates Kramer had brought with him.

The time was some minutes after nine o'clock.

Kramer said, "You'll reach Van Wylie's place around eleven o'clock. You know what to say. You have to convince him that if he doesn't pay up without fuss he'll never see his daughter again. I'm not fooling. If something turns sour, I'll bow out and leave you all to the Cranes. Understand?"

"I understand," Vic said.

"He'll try to find out who you are," Kramer went on. "If he does find out and traces you here, there'll be a massacre." He leaned forward and pointed a thick finger at Vic. "The Cranes don't surrender. They'll kill your wife, your baby and the Van Wylie girl and then they'll fight it out to a finish."

Vic didn't say anything.

"So it is up to you to convince Van Wylie to give you the cheques. When you have them, you will drive to San Bernadino. You'll go to the Chase National Bank and cash the first one. You will then drive to Los Angeles and go to the Merchant Fidelity Bank and cash the second cheque. You'll put up for the night at the Mount Crescent Hotel. I've reserved a room for you in the name of Jack Howard. At eleven o'clock, I'll telephone you. If there are no snags you will go to the Chase National Bank in L.A. and cash the third cheque. From then on you'll drive up the coast, cashing cheques from the list you have. You will finally arrive at 'Frisco. I'll be waiting for you at the Rose Arms

98

Hotel. You'll hand over the money to me and then you are free to return here. By the time you get back, Miss Van Wylie will have been released and the rest of my people will have gone. From then on, you say and do nothing. To you, this has never happened. But if you start acting smart and imagine you can give us away to the Feds, one day someone will arrive at your home and he will wipe you, your wife and baby out. That's a promise. Understand?"

"Yes, I understand," Vic said woodenly.

"Well, that's it . . . don't say you haven't been warned." Kramer got to his feet. "The car's ready. It's time you got off."

Vic stood up.

"My wife is afraid of being alone. What guarantee have I that nothing happens to her while I am away and while you're not here?"

"My dear fella," Kramer said with his expansive insincere smile, "you have nothing to worry about. He's here." He waved to Moe. "The Cranes may be a little wild, but our friend here can control them. Anyway, so long as you do as you're told and Mrs. Dermott doesn't attempt to run away, there is no possible danger to her or your baby."

Vic had to be content with that.

His bag was packed and he was ready to go. He dreaded saying goodbye to Carrie but when he walked into the bedroom, he found her calm and she even managed a smile.

"It's all right, Vic," she said putting her arms around him. "I'm over my fright now. I know it's the only thing for you to do. Don't worry about me. I'll manage."

"I'll get back as soon as I can," Vic said, fondling her. "It'll work out all right. This is something we'll talk about for the rest of our days."

Kramer came to the door.

"Ready to go, Mr. Dermott?"

Vic kissed his son, kissed Carrie, looked long and earnestly at her, then pulling away from her and picking up his bag, he followed Kramer to the front door.

Lifting Junior from his cot, Carrie sat on the bed, her heart cold and frightened, and hugged the baby to her.

On the highway leading to Arrow Lake, Kramer, who had been following Vic's Cadillac in his hired car, tapped his horn button, waved his hand, then branched off on to the secondary road that led to his hotel. Vic saw him go in the driving mirror and continued on his way until in his turn, he turned off the highway and headed for the Van Wylies' estate.

Ten minutes later, he pulled up the electrified gate, got out of the car and went across to the telephone box. A man's voice answered as soon as he had lifted the receiver.

"A caller here for Mr. Van Wylie," Vic said. "He's expecting me. It is to do with Miss Van Wylie."

"Come right on up," the man said curtly.

As Vic replaced the receiver, he heard a click and saw the gate swing back. He got in his car and drove up the twisting drive until he finally reached the main entrance to the big house.

Merrill Andrews was waiting at the top of the steps. He and Vic regarded each other as Vic came up the steps. Andrews was startled to see such a man as Vic. He was expecting some thug: not only surprised, but puzzled as he had a sudden idea he had seen this man somewhere before.

"My business is with Mr. Van Wylie," Vic said.

"This way," Andrews said and strode across a big lobby, through a room lined with books and out on to a paved patio where John Van Wylie was waiting.

As Vic came into the strong sunlight, Van Wylie, dressed in a white shirt, black riding breeches and polished knee-high boots, turned to stare at him. With a flick of his hand, Van Wylie dismissed Andrews, then walking to the garden table, he took from a box a cigar which he lit before saying, "Well? Who are you and what do you want?"

"You and I, Mr. Van Wylie," Vic said quietly, "are in the same position. We both have people we love in danger. My wife and baby are in the hands of the men who have kidnapped your daughter. I am more concerned with their safety than I am with your daughter's."

Van Wylie studied Vic for a long moment, then he waved to a basket chair. "Sit down . . . you talk. I'll listen."

"These people have picked on me to persuade you to part with four million dollars," Vic said, sitting down. "Yesterday, they arrived at my house with your daughter and took over. If I don't get the money from you, they intend to murder your daughter, my wife and baby. These people don't bluff. I have seen them . . . you haven't. There's a young thug with them who could be capable of any cruelty. I think he has already murdered my servant."

"Where is your house?" Van Wylie asked.

"I have been warned that if I tell you who I am and where I live, my wife and baby will suffer," Vic said. "This is no idle threat. I can tell you nothing about myself: all I can tell you is that if you want your daughter back unharmed, you must give me ten certified cheques for four hundred thousand dollars each cheque."

Van Wylie turned away and walked to the end of the patio, blowing a stream of cigar smoke through his nostrils. Vic waited. After a few moments, Van Wylie turned and came back.

"I guess you realize you're making yourself an accessory to a capital crime?" he asked, standing over Vic and glaring at him. "When this is over and the police move in, you could land up in the gas chamber."

"I don't give a damn if I land up the middle of the Pacific," Vic said quietly. "All I'm concerned about is keeping my wife and kid safe."

Van Wylie was now staring at the livid bruise down the side of Vic's face.

"How did you get that?" he demanded, pointing.

"From the young thug I told you about," Vic said. "He wraps a bicycle chain around his fist and then he hits you . . . it's some sock."

Van Wylie took the cigar from his lips, stared at it in disgust and then dropped it into the ash-tray.

"This thug," Vic went on, "is capable of driving his mailed fist into my baby's face or into my wife's face or even into your daughter's face. You have plenty of money. So let's have it! Ten certified cheques for four hundred thousand. I don't see any reason, except pride, why you are hesitating.

If your daughter gets a punch in the face from this thug, she won't have much face left. I'm not just talking, Mr. Van Wylie, I am giving you the stark facts."

"How do I know, if I give you the money, I'll get my daughter back?" Van Wylie asked, putting his blunt, powerful hands on the table and leaning forward to stare at Vic.

"You don't know: as I don't know when I get back, I won't find my wife and baby dead," Vic said, "but that's the way it is. You have plenty of money. If you want to gamble on getting your daughter back, you have the answer."

"I haven't the answer," Van Wylie said and sat down in a basket chair opposite Vic's. "I can give you the money, but I still don't know what I'm buying."

Vic made an impatient movement. He didn't say anything.

After a pause, Van Wylie said, "You have seen my daughter? She's all right?"

"Yes, I've seen her, and as far as I know right now she is all right."

"Tell me about these people who have kidnapped her. How many are there?"

"My business with you is to persuade you to give me the ransom money," Vic said. "I have been warned to give you no information. All you have to do is to decide whether you are paying up or whether you are going to leave your daughter in the hands of these people. That's all."

Van Wylie stared at him, his hard eyes probing, then he nodded and got to his feet.

"Wait here. I'll fix it."

He walked quickly across the patio and into the study where Andrews was waiting.

Van Wylie issued his orders and Andrews got busy on the telephone. He spoke to the manager of the California and Merchant Bank. The manager, sounding a little startled, said he would have the certified cheques ready in an hour.

"This guy isn't one of them," Van Wylie said as Andrews replaced the receiver. "They are using him as their stooge

... smart. He has a wife and baby. They've moved into his house with Zelda. He has to collect the money. If there is a slip up, they'll take it out of his family."

"I've seen him before," Andrews said. "I'm trying to remember who he is ... someone: a personality. I think he's to do with the theatre."

Van Wylie sat on the edge of the desk. His small hard eyes were bleak as he looked at Andrews.

"They've knocked him around. Did you see the bruise on his face? These punks aren't made of custard." He leaned forward. "Where have you seen him before?"

"I don't know," Andrews said. "But I'm sure I have seen him. He's someone who's been in the news."

"That helps a lot, doesn't it?" Van Wylie said, a snarl in his voice. "You think! I want to know who he is!"

Andrews walked over to the window and stared out. Where had he seen this man before? Why did he connect him with the theatre? Was he an actor? He was still standing there, digging into his memory when Van Wylie with a snort of impatience went back to where Vic was waiting.

Moe was like a flea on a hot stove. He couldn't relax: he couldn't concentrate: all he could think about was his mother. What was happening to her? he kept asking himself. Was she any better? Was she dying? From time to time, he looked longingly at the telephone, longing to pick up the receiver and call the hospital, but he knew such a call could spell disaster. If by chance Van Wylie had alerted the Feds and they traced the call to Wastelands, his chance of gaining a quarter of a million dollars would go up in gunsmoke.

But he had to know!

Zelda and Carrie were together with the baby in the bedroom. He could hear them talking. The Cranes were lolling in the sun, drinking Cokes and looking through the comics Riff had found in the ranch house. The setup seemed peaceful enough. Moe struggled with the temptation. He knew he would be going against Kramer's orders, but he had to get to a telephone where he could talk to the hospital and find out how his mother was. He just couldn't go on waiting and hoping. He had to know!

The nearest call booth was at Boston Creek, a twenty-mile drive. If he drove fast, he could go and return in just, over the hour. What could happen in that time? Sweating, nervous and anxious, he got to his feet. He had to go!

The Cranes looked up as Moe came out of the ranch house and headed towards them. ,

As Moe reached them, he said. "I've a little business to fix. I'll be right back. You two stick around. There's to be no trouble. Just see the two girls remain right where they are." He looked at his watch. "I'll be back in an hour."

"Sure," Riff said and grinned. "We'll be here when you get back. We have no place to go."

Moe stared suspiciously at him.

"You stay right here," he said. "I'm not having any trouble."

"Who's talking about trouble?" Riff said, stretching his powerful frame lazily. "Me . . . I'm enjoying myself. You shove off. We can take care of everything."

Moe, suddenly uneasy as he saw the sneering expression in Riff's eyes, hesitated, but when the Cranes picked up their comics and seemed to forget him, he turned and walked to the garage. He got into the car he had come in, gunned the engine and drove down the dusty drive to the highway.

As his car disappeared in a cloud of dust, Riff dropped his comic, stretched elaborately and then got to his feet. Chita looked at him.

"Where do you think you're going?" she asked, her eyes suspicious.

"Belt up!" Riff snarled. "I'm going to stretch my legs. What's it to you where I go?"

"Skip it, Riff! Sit down! I know what you're planning to do! You cut it out! We're in this racket for ten thousand dollars! You're not going to foul it up!"

Riff grinned at her. "You dope! Can't you see it's fouled up already? I'm going to get me a little fun. You stick here. I won't tell you twice."

"Leave the girl alone!" Chita said, but she didn't move.

Her brother's vicious expression warned her that if she stood up, he would hit her.

"Screw you!" Riff said and hitching up his leather trousers, he swaggered towards the ranch house.

If there was one thing Zelda disliked more than another, it was babies. To her, babies were noisy at one end and wet at the other. To her, they were revolting little animals who always attracted more attention than she ever received, even though she was the third richest girl in the world. Bring a baby on the scene and everyone seemed to forget about her. She hated babies!

She sat sulkily in an armchair and watched Carrie change Junior's nappy. Her nose wrinkled with disgust. Babies! But to be in Vic Dermott's house gave her a tremendous thrill. She had seen every one of his plays. She thought it was frantically romantic that Dermott of all people should be the man to collect her ransom. Vic Dermott! What an endless source of conversation she would have when she finally returned home!

She liked Carrie. It was a pity such an attractive girl should be so obsessed with this fat, dreary baby. She wanted to relax and talk to Carrie about clothes. She was sure Carrie could help her. She had so little confidence in herself in choosing the right things to wear. If only Carrie would quit fussing over this fat little horror, put him away somewhere and concentrate on her, Zelda would be happy.

With relief, she watched Carrie put the baby back in his cot and arrange the small toys hanging above the cot to keep him amused.

"Well, he's fixed for the moment," Carrie said. "Now I guess I'd better straighten this room or maybe you'll do it while I see what there's for lunch."

Zelda stared at her as if she couldn't believe what had been said.

"*I* do it? I don't know what you mean."

"Well, someone's got to keep the place going," Carrie said patiently. "I'm willing to do the cooking. I thought you might straighten the bedrooms. Those two out there aren't likely to do anything."

"I'm not doing anything either!" Zelda said angrily. "I'm not a servant! In a day or so, my father will pay the ransom and I'll return home. What happens here doesn't concern me in the slightest!"

Carrie regarded her thoughtfully.

"Well, of course, if that's how you feel about it," she said, "then I'll do it. I suppose you want to eat?"

"Of course I want to eat!"

The two girls stared at each other, then Carrie shrugged.

"All right, if you just want to sit around, I'll handle it," she said.

"I'm certainly not turning myself into a servant," Zelda exclaimed crossly and looked out of the window.

At this moment, the bedroom door swung open and Riff appeared in the doorway.

Both Carrie and Zelda stiffened as they stared at him. Riff's scarred face was glistening with sweat. Carrie was nearer to him than Zelda. She could smell the dirt from him and she backed away. He wasn't looking at her. He was staring at Zelda who seemed frozen in her chair.

"Come on, baby," Riff said, beckoning to her. "You and me are going to have a jazz session. Get out of that chair!"

Carrie moved in front of Zelda and faced Riff.

"Get out of here!" she said fiercely. "You're not to touch her!"

Riff grinned evilly.

"Out of the way or I'll start on you first!"

Carrie didn't move. She was terrified, but something in her forced her to face this scarred-faced thug.

"Get out!"

Riff's long looping left with his fist half closed caught Carrie on the side of her face. It was as if she had been struck by a tremendous blast of wind. She went reeling across the room, thudded against the bed and fell across it, stunned and only half conscious.

She was vaguely aware that Zelda was screaming. She made a desperate effort to get to her feet, but her legs buckled and she slid from the bed to the floor. Dazed, trying to get up, she watched Zelda struggling with Riff. Zelda was helpless in his savage grip. He swung her off her feet and carried her out of the room. Her screams echoed through the house. Her fists pounded uselessly on the shabby leather uniform. Riff rushed her down the short passage and into the bedroom she occupied. Brutally, he flung her on the bed, then turning, he locked the door. As she scrambled off the bed, her eyes wide with terror, Riff moved in on her. As his hands grabbed her, she began to scream again.

Chita sat motionless in the hot sunshine while she listened to the high-pitched screams coming from the ranch house. She didn't move. She just sat still, her face wooden, her hands clenched between her knees.

After a while the screaming stopped.

Moe Zegetti stood in the telephone booth waiting. Sweat ran down his fat face. Through the glass panel of the booth he watched two girls in tight-fitting, washed-out jeans, sitting on stools, sucking at straws in Coke bottles. A boy with a crew-cut and with freckles across his nose, leaned his elbows on the soda counter and talked to them. He too had a Coke bottle with a straw in it in his hand.

Moe wiped the sweat from his forehead with the back of his hand. How much longer did he have to wait? He could hear the hum over the open line and every now and then, faint voices. He had got through to the hospital. They had told him to hold on. Minutes dragged by. One of the girls at the counter slid off the stool and went over to the juke box. She inserted a coin. As the juke box began to blare jazz, she began to swing her small, childish hips and snap her fingers while her companion and the boy watched her, grinning.

A voice said, "Mr. Zegetti? This is Nurse Hardisty. I'm sorry to tell you your mother passed away peacefully last night."

The strident sound from the juke box came through the glass panel of the booth and swamped Moe's isolation. He found it impossible to hear what the woman was saying. He pressed the receiver to his ear, his heart thumping. He couldn't really have heard aright . . . his mother . . . passed away . . . that meant she was dead!

"What was that?" he demanded. "Hold on a moment." He opened the booth door and bawled, "Turn that goddam thing off!"

The girl stopped dancing and stared at him. The other girl and the boy turned and stared too. Then the girl started dancing again, giggling and rotating her hips at Moe and went hip-swinging down to the entrance door, snapping her fingers and singing.

In despair, Moe slammed the booth door shut.

"How's my mother?" he shouted frantically above the noise of the music.

"I told you." The nurse sounded impatient. "She passed peacefully . . ."

"You mean she's dead?"

"Why, yes, of course. I'm telling you . . . she died last night."

Slowly, Moe replaced the receiver. He leaned against the wall of the booth and closed his eyes. A bluebottle fly buzzed busily around and about him. The girl wriggled her slight body as her companion and the boy began to clap their hands in time with the music.

Moe suddenly had no further wish to own a quarter of a million dollars. What use would the money be to him now? He was alone. He'd always be alone now Doll was dead. With her, it would have been fun to have had money to burn, but without her . . .

He walked slowly from the café, unaware that the barman and the three young people were staring curiously at him, and he sat in the car, his hands resting slackly on the driving wheel. Should he go back to Wastelands? Suppose something went wrong? Kramer was old: suppose his planning came adrift? Moe thought of those awful years in prison. What would he do with a quarter of million dollars anyway? But then he thought of the little restaurant and the long hours of slavery. He couldn't go back there. With money he could buy himself a small house. He could live decently. He might even find some woman with whom he could share his life. Besides, he couldn't let Kramer down. No ... he had to go back. Kramer would never forgive him if he ducked out now.

With a gesture of despair, he drove the car on to the highway and headed back towards Wastelands.

"You still don't remember where you've seen him before?" Van Wylie asked. He was standing at the window watching Vic Dermott as he got into his Cadillac. Vic was on his way down to the California and Merchant Bank to pick up the certified cheques.

"No ... but I'm sure I've seen him some place," Andrews returned. "I'm sure of that and I'm sure he's something to do with the theatre."

"You got his car number?"

"Sure."

The Cadillac was now out of sight. For a long moment, Van Wylie stood thinking.

"Okay, now let's get busy," he said. "If these punks think they're going to get away with four millions of my dollars, they're in for a surprise. They said they'd tapped the telephone here. Could be bluff, but I'm not taking any risk. Jay Dennison is the boy we want. Send him a Telex. Tell him to meet me at the L.A. airport at twelve. Warn him it's to be a secret meeting. We'll take the helicopter. They won't be able to follow us in that. Get moving."

An hour and a half later, Van Wylie with Andrews at his heels, strode across the tarmac of the airport and into a small office where Jay Dennison had arranged to meet him. With Dennison was Tom Harper.

It was some years since Van Wylie and Dennison had met. Then Dennison had saved Van Wylie a considerable sum of money when he had exposed a bank fraud by a brilliant piece of detective work. Van Wylie hadn't forgotten Dennison's work, and every Christmas, Dennison had received a large food hamper with Van Wylie's compliments.

The two men shook hands and Dennison was quick to see the hard bitter gleam in Van Wylie's eyes.

"My daughter has been kidnapped," Van Wylie said

abruptly as he sat on the edge of the desk. "The ransom is for four million dollars with the usual threats if I go to the police I won't get her back. I'm consulting you, Dennison, because as soon as I do get her back, I want you to get these hoodlums. We flew here. They have no means of knowing we have met, and they mustn't know." He took from his pocket a small reel of tape. "I recorded the man's demands. You'd better have this," and he handed the reel of tape to Dennison.

"When did this happen, Mr. Van Wylie?" Dennison asked, sitting behind the desk. He glanced at Harper who had his notebook ready.

With lucid detail, Van Wylie stated the facts while Dennison listened. Finally, Van Wylie came to Vic Dermott's part in the kidnapping.

"It's obvious this fella has nothing to do with the kidnappers," Van Wylie said. "He's in as bad a fix as I am. Andrews here thinks he has seen him before."

Dennison looked sharply at Andrews.

"I'm trying to remember just where, but I can't place him," Andrews said in his slow drawl. "I'm sure he's something to do with the theatre . . . maybe an actor. I'm quite sure he isn't a movie actor . .. he's to do with the theatre."

"Well, that's something to go on," Dennison said and reached for the telephone. He got through to the Field Office at Paradise City and spoke to Abe Mason. "I'm sending along a Mr. Merrill Andrews. He'll be with you within an hour. He'll explain. I want you to call up Simons and Ley, the theatrical agents. Get them to let you have photographs of every actor around thirty-eight years of age, around six foot tall, dark, they have on their books. This is a rush job." He hung up and looked at Andrews. Would get off. Mr. Andrews? There's a chance you'll spot the guy from the photographs my man will show you."

Andrews looked inquiringly at Van Wylie. At his nod, he hurried from the office.

"The kidnappers are dangerous," Van Wylie said. "I don't want Zelda to run any risk. You understand?"

"Of course," Dennison said quietly. "We know how to

handle this. Let's have some more facts about her routine. You say she always went to the hairdresser's at the same time and on the same day?"

An hour later, Van Wylie got to his feet.

"That's about it," he said. "I'll leave it to you, but you don't make any moves without first consulting me."

"That's understood," Dennison returned, getting to his feet and shaking hands.

Van Wylie stared at him for a long moment.

"I'd rather lose four million dollars than Zelda," he said, "She's all I've got to live for now."

When he had gone, Dennison reached for the telephone.

At the Field Office, Merrill Andrews tossed the last photograph on Abe Mason's desk with an exclamation of disgust.

"No . . . he's not among this lot," he said.

"Maybe he's a movie actor," Mason said. "I can get . . ."

"He's not a movie actor," Andrews broke in. "I'm as sure as I sit here, he's to do with the theatre and well known at that."

"Okay," Mason said, getting to his feet. "We'll go over to the *Herald's* office and look through their photographs. They have a library of famous people. Maybe we'll spot him there."

As they were leaving the building, they ran into Dennison who had driven fast from the airport.

"Any luck?" Dennison asked, pausing.

Mason explained where they were going, and Dennison nodded. He went up to his office and put through a call to the San Bernadino police. He asked if any patrol officer on the highway leading from the Van Wylie estate to San Bernadino had seen Miss Van Wylie around nine o'clock the previous day. The sergeant in charge said he would call back.

Dennison then asked the sergeant to alert every patrol officer to look out for a Jaguar E-type car and gave Zelda's licence number.

That done, he got Harper to check on the licence number of the Cadillac that Andrews had given him.

"No such number," Harper said as he hung up the telephone receiver.

Dennison grunted. He pulled a tape recorder towards him and wound on the reel of tape that Van Wylie had given him.

The two men listened to the voice. After playing the tape back three times, Dennison turned the machine off. He reached for a cigar, lit it and relaxed back in his chair.

"Know anyone who binds his fist with a bicycle chain as a weapon?" he asked suddenly.

"About a couple of hundred by name," Harper said cynically. "There are probably twenty or thirty thousand who I don't know. It's the latest fad with these beats.

"Yeah, but this isn't small-time, Tom. Four million dollars! That was an old man's voice." Dennison blew smoke up to the ceiling. "It takes my mind back to the old days when gangsters really asked big money for a ransom. You know, it's the kind of job that Jim Kramer might pull if he was crazy enough to come out of retirement. Knowing Kramer the way I do, I can't believe he would try a kidnapping. Send a Telex to every bank in the state, telling them to report when someone cashes a bearer cheque, signed by John Van Wylie for four hundred thousand dollars. We may be a little late, but we might just possibly catch up with this guy, cashing the cheques."

Harper nodded and left the room.

Dennison smoked on, his eyes blank, his face expressionless. Kramer! Could just possibly be. He had vanished. Moe Zegetti who always worked with him had also vanished. Dennison's face suddenly twisted in to a grim smile. If it was Kramer and they caught him, he would have the satisfaction of seeing Kramer go to the gas chamber. No Federal Officer could wish for a nicer retiring present than that!

CHAPTER EIGHT

I<small>T</small> was Junior's nagging cry that made Carrie get unsteadily to her feet. Her face felt hot and puffy where Riff had hit her. Silence brooded over the house, except for Junior's crying. She picked the baby up and held him close to her. Satisfied that he was getting the attention he needed, Junior stopped crying and began to make chortling noises.

Carrie carried him out into the lobby and stood, listening. She heard nothing. She went to the front door, opened it and looked out into the patio.

Chita was looking in her direction as she sat in the sunlight. Huskily, Carrie said, "You'd better come . . . please."

Chita looked indifferently at her.

"Keep out of it," she said. "You'll only get hurt."

"But you can't let him . . ."

"Go back to your room."

Carrie went back to her room. She put Junior into his cot, and with an unsteady hand she gave him one of his favourite toys, then with a rapidly beating heart, she walked to Zelda's room. This was probably the bravest thing she had ever done in her life. The thought of having to face Riff again terrified her, but she couldn't leave Zelda defenceless to cope with him alone. She turned the door handle, but the door was locked.

She hesitated, then she began hammering on the door with her clenched fists.

"Open this door!" she shouted, her voice unsteady with terror.

The silence from the room horrified her. Maybe this awful savage had killed the girl!

She hammered on the door again.

"Zelda! Are you all right! Open this door!"

There was a long pause of silence, then Carrie heard whispering. Then she heard Zelda giggle. The sound came as such a shock to her that she felt the blood leave her face.

"It's all right," Zelda called. "Do go away!"

As Carrie remained motionless, aware of her thudding heartbeats, she heard a sound behind her and she looked around.

Chita had come silently into the house. She stood glaring at Carrie. Her expression was something that Carrie hoped never to see on a woman's face again. There was pain, anger, frustration and bitter jealousy that had turned Chita's face into a mask of despair.

"What are you worrying about, you poor fool?" Chita demanded, her voice shaking with pent-up fury. "My brother has a way with women! Get away! Go back to your room!"

Sickened, Carrie walked past her and entered her room. She closed the door, her hand against her aching face. With a shiver of disgust, she locked herself in.

Patrol Officer Murphy walked into Jay Dennison's office. He saluted as he said, "Murphy, 'D' Division. Sergeant O'Harridon told me to report, sir."

"Miss Van Wylie?" Dennison asked, pushing aside the papers on his desk.

"That's right, sir," Murphy went quickly over the facts. "There was this other girl with her, sir," he went on. "She was something a bit different." He gave a detailed description of Chita. "I got the idea Miss Van Wylie was giving this girl a lift into town."

Dennison asked a number of questions. By the time he had finished with Murphy he had all the information he could get from the Patrol Officer.

"I followed Miss Van Wylie as far as the Macklin Square car park," Murphy concluded. "I left her there."

"Okay," Dennison said. "You'd be able to identify this other girl again?"

"Sure would."

Dennison dismissed Murphy with a wave of his hand after cautioning him not to talk. He then called the San Bernadino police headquarters. He asked them to check the Macklin Square car park. He said he had an idea they would find Miss Van Wylie's Jaguar there. The sergeant in charge said he would call back.

Merrill Andrews and Abe Mason came in as Dennison replaced the telephone receiver.

"We've been through every photograph in the *Herald's* library," Mason said. "Mr. Andrews isn't sure, but he thinks he's spotted the man we're after." He put a photograph of a group of men on Dennison's desk. "This photograph is of the cast of a play called 'Moonlight in Venice.' The man in the last row, third from the right, is Victor Dermott who wrote the play. Mr. Andrews has an idea he's our man."

"Yeah," Andrews joined in. "It's a bad photo, but he certainly looks like the guy."

Dennison reached for the telephone. He asked to be connected with Mr. Simon of Simon and Ley, the theatrical agents. After a long wait, Simon came on the line. He knew Dennison, but he seemed surprised to have a call from the inspector.

"Sorry to worry you, Mr. Simon," Dennison said. "I want to get in touch with Mr. Victor Dermott. Can you give me his address?"

"I guess I can give you his home address," Simon said cautiously. "but I don't think you'll find him at home. He's away some place. What's it all about?"

"It's urgent and confidential," Dennison said. "I'd be glad of your help."

Seconds later, after making a note on a scratch pad, Dennison said, "Thanks: sorry to have bothered you," and he hung up.

"The address is 13345 Lincoln Avenue, Los Angeles," he told Mason. "Take Mr. Andrews and go out there. Ask for Mr. Dermott. See if you can get a good photograph of him if he isn't at home. If he is our man, find out where he is."

As Andrews and Mason left the office, Tom Harper came in.

"Report on the Telex from Chase National, San Bernadino and Merchant Fidelity of Los Angeles," he said. "They have cashed bearer cheques for four hundred thousand dollars, signed by Van Wylie."

"Any description of the man who cashed them?"

"Yeah . . . the same. He's around thirty-eight, tall, good-looking and dark. Well dressed."

Dennison thought for a long moment, then he said, "I have a special job for you, Tom. Go out to Arrowhead Lake. I want you to check all the hotels in the district. See if you can find out if a man answering Jim Kramer's description is staying or has stayed at any of the hotels. Be careful how you make your inquiries. Get Kramer's photo from our files. Take Letts and Brody with you. I want a report back fast."

Harper forgot himself for a moment, to say, "Jim Kramer? You don't mean . . . ?"

Dennison stared at him.

"I said report back fast!"

"Yes, sir," Harper said hurriedly and left the office at a run.

"Carrie!"

Zelda's voice floated across the lobby and Carrie, who had been bathing her aching face, came out of the bathroom and to her bedroom door.

"Carrie!"

She unlocked the door and moved out into the lobby.

"Yes?"

"Will you come?"

Carrie assured herself that Junior was amusing himself, then she walked across the lobby to Zelda's room. The door stood open. She hesitated a moment, then went in.

Zelda was sitting on the side of her bed which was in disorder. She was wrapped in a sheet. Her usually immaculate hair was tousled. Her face was flushed and her eyes reminded Carrie of the eyes of a cat that had satisfied itself with too much cream.

Carrie glanced quickly around the room. There was no sign of Riff Crane. By the bed were the remains of Zelda's clothes. The dress she had been wearing lay in two pieces. White rags represented her underwear.

"I haven't any clothes," Zelda said very calmly. "Could you lend me some?"

"Are you hurt?" Carrie asked anxiously. "Where – where is he?"

Zelda giggled and blushed.

"I'm fine . . . he's taking a bath. I persuaded him." She nodded to the closed door of the bathroom. "Oh, Carrie! I must tell someone! I'm wild about him!" She closed her eyes, her expression ecstatic. Carrie felt a sudden impulse to smack her face, but she controlled herself. "You don't know! He's marvellous. He's so – so primitive! Carrie! I'm in love with him! He's the first man who really means something to me! I'm going to marry him!"

"Have you gone mad?" Carrie exclaimed. "How can you think of such a thing! Look at me! He hit me! Look at my face!"

Simpering, Zelda pulled aside the sheet to reveal a livid purple bruise on the side of her thigh.

"He hit me, too. He's like that. He doesn't know his own strength. He takes what he wants . . . brutally . . . marvellously . . . He . . ."

"Stop it, you stupid little fool!" Carrie cried, revolted. "A brute like that! You must be out of your mind!"

Zelda's face hardened and she pouted.

"You needn't be jealous," she said. "I know he preferred me to you, but what can you expect? After all, you're older and you have a baby . . . Riff wouldn't want a woman . . ."

Carrie said dangerously. "If you don't stop it, I'm going to slap you . . . I mean just that."

The bathroom door swung open and Riff stood in the doorway. He had a towel draped around his middle. His massive muscular chest was black with coarse thick hair. His arms also sprouted black hair. To Carrie, he looked like a terrifying ape. She moved back towards the door.

"Hello, baby," Riff said, grinning at her. "You still around, looking for trouble?"

"Oh, leave her alone, Riff," Zelda said, looking adoringly at him. "She's only jealous. She wouldn't dare do a thing to me with you around." To Carrie, she went on, "Please let me have some clothes," She simpered. "Riff was in such a hurry, he – he ripped everything of mine to bits."

Riff leered at Carrie.

"Fix her up with something," he said and laughed. "We've taken a fancy to each other."

Her face coldly horrified, Carrie waved to the row of closets.

"Take what you want," she said and went quickly out of the room.

Riff wandered over to the dressing-table. He picked up a cut-glass bottle of toilet water. He slapped the toilet water onto his chest, sniffing appreciatively.

"I smell like a tart now," he said, grinning. "You like me this way?"

Zelda looked adoringly at him.

"I think you're marvellous, Riff. Those muscles . . . you . . ."

"Yeah, yeah, yeah. You get some clothes on, baby. I'll be back," and winking, he went out of the room, closing the door. Barefooted and with only the towel around his middle, he went out into the hot sunshine.

Chita stood waiting for him. Her back rested against the veranda rail, a cigarette hung from her lips, her face was a cold, hostile mask.

Riff padded towards her, grinning gleefully.

"Baby, we're on the gravy train." He kept his voice low. "This stupid cow has fallen for me! Can you imagine? Ten thousand bucks! That's a real laugh now. She wants to marry me!"

Chita lost colour. Her eyes glittered.

"Marry *you*! What do you mean?"

Riff was excited. He sat down in the basket chair near Chita and moved his thick fingers through his hair.

"What I'm telling you. I've only just found out who she is. Her old man is one of the richest punks in the world! He owns half Texas, goddam it! That's why Kramer was smart enough to snatch her! Now listen, she's gone soppy about me. She's the type who likes it rough." His savage, scarred face lit up with a leering grin. "And baby! Did I give it to her rough; I had her . . ."

"Shut up, you stinker!" Chita shouted at him. "Marry *you*! You stupid hunk-head! You imagine her old man would let you marry *her*! You're crazy!"

Riff's leg shot out. He hooked his foot around Chita's ankles and she came down heavily on the end of her spine. The shock drove the breath out of her body and Riff, leaning forward, slapped her across her face.

He jumped to his feet, his face ugly with fury as she half tried to get up.

"Want more?" he snarled. "You can have it! Keep your mouth shut! Now you listen to what I'm telling you. Hear me?"

Chita sank back. The marks of Riff's thick fingers made white weals on her face.

"This is where we cash in," Riff said, sitting down again. "Can't you see? That guy Kramer had a nerve to offer us only ten thousand! That's peanuts! And besides, this job could turn sour. I've thought it all out. All we now have to do is to get the car and take the girl back to her old man. That'll put us clear of the snatch. He'll be so grateful, he won't take police action. Then she'll tell him she loves me." He grinned. "She'll tell him there's a baby on the way. So what can he do? Whether he likes it or not, he's got to say okay, and then, baby, we'll have all the money in the world! Married to that little cow means we get our hooks on the old man's dough . . . he's worth millions!"

"I'm not marrying her," Chita said quietly. "So what happens to me?"

Riff scowled at her.

"What's the matter with you? You come along for the ride. What do you think happens to you?"

"The three of us, is that it? She'll love that. I'll love it too!"

"She'll do what I tell her!"

"But I won't!"

Riff made an exasperated gesture with his hands.

"You want to spend her money, don't you?"

Chita leaned forward. Her face, still showing the four livid marks of Riff's fingers, was vicious.

"No, I don't! We've been together ever since we were born! We've done everything together! We've had fun together! I'm not sharing you with any other woman! I'm not letting that poor fool with all her money come between us!"

"You talk as if you were my wife," Riff snarled. "Have you gone nuts or something?"

Chita stared at him. "Well, aren't I your wife?"

"You! You're crazy! What do you mean . . . you're my sister! What are you talking about?"

"I am also your wife," Chita said.

Riff tried to meet her steady, furious gaze, but he couldn't do it. He looked away.

"Don't bring that up," he muttered and got to his feet. "That's only happened once and you know it was your fault. You're my sister! My wife! You're nuts!"

"Oh, Riff . . ."

They both looked quickly down the veranda to where Zelda was standing. She had on a lemon-coloured shir t, pair of scarlet, tight-fitting slacks and she had bound a white scarf around her hair. Her expression was so animated she almost looked beautiful.

"When are we leaving, Riff?"

"Just as soon as I get some clothes on," Riff said.

"I've found you something to wear," Zelda said. "I've laid them out on the bed. Hurry, Riff. I want to leave as quickly as I can."

Chita said in a cold, flat voice, "There's a car coming."

Riff turned quickly and stared down the long dirt road. He stood tense for a few moments watching the approaching car.

"It's Zegetti!" Riff exclaimed.

"This should be fun," Chita said. "What are you going to tell him about taking her home?"

Riff ran quickly down the veranda and into Zelda's bedroom. Quickly, he picked up his black leather trousers which he had flung on the floor. He put his hand in one of the hip pockets for Vic's gun, but it wasn't there. A quick search, amid a stream of obscene cursing, confirmed the gun had vanished!

Vera Synder, a large comfortable-looking woman with grey hair, whose pleasant face now carried an expression of alert curiosity, had been Vic Dermott's secretary for the past five years.

She sat behind her large desk and regarded Abe Mason and Merrill Andrews through big horn-rimmed spectacles as she said. "Federal Bureau, Mr. Mason? I don't understand."

"Can you please tell me where I can find Mr. Dermott?" Mason repeated politely.

"You asked that question just now. I said I don't understand. What business have you with Mr. Dermott?"

While they were talking, Andrews was looking around the big, pleasantly-furnished room. He saw at the far end of the room a photograph of a man in a silver frame. He got abruptly to his feet, walked the length of the room and stared at the excellent likeness of Dermott, then he turned and said excitedly, "It's Dermott all right! No possible mistake about it!"

Mason relaxed. Now at last they were getting somewhere. To Miss Synder, he said, "This is an urgent police matter. It is essential we get in touch with Mr. Dermott right away. Please tell me where he is."

"Mr. Dermott is writing a play," Miss Synder said with determination. "He is not to be disturbed. I have no authority to give you his address."

Mason restrained his impatience with difficulty.

"Mr. Dermott could be in very great danger," he said quietly. "We have reason to believe that kidnappers have moved into the house where he is living and are threatening the lives of his wife and baby."

Vic had often said that if an atomic bomb went off behind Miss Synder's chair, she would be completely unruffled. She was unruffled now.

"May I see your credentials, Mr. Mason?"

With a suppressed grunt of exasperation, Mason handed over his warrant card. Miss Synder examined it and then returned it.

Three minutes later, Mason was on the telephone to Dennison.

"It's Dermott all right," he said. "He and his wife have rented a ranch house called Wastelands from a Mr. and Mrs. Harris-Jones. The house is completely isolated: about twenty miles from a little place called Boston Creek and some fifty miles from Pitt City."

"Good work," Dennison said. "Come on back. We don't need Mr. Andrews any more. Get back here as fast as you can."

As Dennison replaced the receiver, the telephone bell began to ring. With an impatient movement, he lifted the receiver again. It was Sergeant O'Harridon of the San Bernadino police.

"We've found Miss Van Wylie's Jag," he reported. "It was where you said. One interesting point: the passenger door has been sprayed with some pretty strong acid. It's eaten away all the leather work."

"Get every fingerprint you can find on the car," Dennison ordered. "Let me know what acid has been used."

"The boys are working on it now," O'Harridon said and hung up.

As Dennison reached for a cigar, the telephone rang again. It was Tom Harper.

"Hit the jackpot right away, Chief," Harper said. "Kramer stayed two days at the Lake Arrowhead Hotel. The doorman identified him from the photograph. Three o'clock on the day of the kidnapping, Kramer hired a convertible Buick and drove away, heading towards Pitt City. He didn't return that night, but he arrived back at the hotel the following morning soon after eleven o'clock. He paid his check, handed over the Buick and took a taxi to the railroad station. He was in time to catch the 'Frisco train."

"Good work," Dennison said. "So it looks as if it could be Kramer at the back of this. Now look, Tom, I have a job for you as you are out there on the spot. We're pretty sure Miss Van Wylie is at a ranch house called Wastelands." He described where Wastelands was located. "But I'm not absolutely sure she is there. I want you to find out. Think you can do it?"

"I guess so," Harper said without much enthusiasm.

"You've got to be surer than that," Dennison said, a sudden edge to his voice. "These hoods mustn't be alerted. They could be killers. I know they are acid throwers. If they suspect we are on to them, they could massacre the girl, the Dermotts and anyone else there who could identify them." While he was talking, he was thinking. "Hang on a moment." He put down the receiver, lit his cigar while he continued to think. Then, picking up the receiver, he said, "Here's what you do, Tom. Hire a car. Leave your wallet, your warrant and your gun with Brody. Drive out to Wastelands, take a look at the place, then ring on the front door bell. Tell whoever answers the door that you are a friend of the Harris-Jones and they are letting you hire the house in a couple of months' time. As you happen to be passing, could you look over the house and see if it is suitable for your requirements . . . you know the blah. Keep your eyes open. They won't let you in, but you'll get an idea of the geography of the place. Let me know what outbuildings there are: what cover there is: if we can get a bunch of men near enough to the house to rush it. You know the sort of thing I want. And watch out, Tom: these hoods are dangerous if Kramer is hooked up with them."

"Okay, Chief," Harper said. "I'll get moving right away. I should be out there by five o'clock. Should I take either Letts or Brody with me?"

"What for?" Dennison said impatiently. "Do you imagine you're going to feel lonely?"

Moe Zegetti had taken his time about returning to

Wastelands. When he was clear of Boston Creek, he had pulled up by the side of the road, prepared to give way to his grief.

To his surprise the tears he was expecting didn't come, for he suddenly realized what his mother's passing really meant to him. He realized for the first time in his life he would be able to do exactly what he wanted to do without having to consult his mother first. This unexpected realization startled him and he lit a cigarette and considered, not without a twinge of guilt, just what this discovery could mean to his future.

He was forty-eight years of age. He had never married because his mother had never approved of any girl he had brought home for her inspection. All his life he had been under his mother's domination. There had been times when she had driven him half crazy with her bossy ways. Among many irritating things, she had insisted that he should change his shirt every day and that he should limit his drinking and so on and so on. With a quarter of a million dollars coming to him, he would have a new, free and exciting life to look forward to. Still thinking about himself as he sat in the car, he realized that when his mother hadn't been bossing him around, Kramer had. He had to admit that when Kramer had walked out on him, his affairs had turned sour, but that hadn't been really his fault. He had had bad luck. Now Kramer was back, bossing him around again! Moe moved restlessly. A quarter of a million dollars! It was nice money, but why had Kramer offered him such a sum? Just how much was Kramer going to get out of this snatch? If Kramer was willing to part with a quarter of a million, it was a safe bet that Kramer himself was going to pick up at least three or possibly four million!

Influenced by this new heady feeling of freedom, Moe decided the split wasn't fair. Although Kramer had planned the job, he, Moe, had been landed with the dangerous end. If the job happened to turn sour, he would be the first to take the rap. It wasn't good enough. When Kramer began to dish out the money, Moe told himself, he would be a sucker if he didn't ask for more. He might even persuade Kramer to split the take.

With these thoughts running through his head, Moe started the car and drove towards Wastelands. During the drive, he brooded about the ransom. He finally convinced himself that Kramer must split the money with him. He would tell Kramer he, Moe, would be willing to pay off the Cranes from his share, but Kramer would have to accept the new terms. In this mood of elation, Moe didn't even consider just how he would persuade Kramer to do this.

It was because his native cunning was alerted by these thoughts that he immediately sensed that something was wrong as he pulled up outside the ranch house.

He sat for a long moment in the car, looking towards the veranda. Zelda, in a new outfit, with Chita was standing tense and looking towards him. There was no sign of Riff.

He got out of the car. Something was up, he told himself, but what? The Cranes were tricky, but for all their trickiness, he couldn't imagine what they had been up to to give him this feeling of uneasiness. Casually, he undid the button of his jacket to enable him to get at the .38 automatic he carried in a holster under his jacket.

He walked slowly to the steps of the veranda and mounted them.

"All okay?" he asked, pausing at the top of the steps and staring at Chita.

He saw Zelda glance swiftly at Chita and then away.

Chita said, "Why shouldn't it be?"

There was something about her expression that made him uneasy. He saw too that the left side of her face was slightly bruised.

"Where's Riff?" he asked without moving.

"Inside," Chita said.

There was a pause as Moe stared searchingly at her, then Riff appeared in the front doorway. He was wearing his black leather suit. There was sweat on his face and his smile was a fixed grimace.

"Hyah, there," he said. "So you're back."

"Where's Mrs. Dermott?" Moe asked, turning so he faced Riff.

"Inside with her brat," Riff said.

Moe suddenly noticed that Riff's hand was out of sight, behind his back.

"Everything okay while I've been away?" he asked.

"Sure . . . fine," Riff said and he began to move towards Moe.

Out of the corner of his eye, Moe was aware that Chita was moving casually, but her languid strides were bringing her quickly towards him.

"What have you behind your back?" Moe asked.

"What are you talking about?" Riff asked. He was nearly within striking distance of Moe.

Moe hadn't been considered by the police as a dangerous criminal for nothing. He may have allowed himself to be bossed around by his mother and by Kramer, but when in a tight spot, Moe could be as dangerous as a rattlesnake. As Kramer's lieutenant, he had had control of young vicious hoods who could turn into killers and he had never lost in a show-down. He had the knack of drawing a gun faster than any of the hoods he handled. It was a knack that had saved his life many times in the past and a knack he had never let get rusty.

Riff, his hand bound in his chain, was about to deal Moe a crushing blow to his face when he found himself looking at the vicious nose of a .38 that had appeared in Moe's hand as if by magic.

Seeing the gun, Chita stopped as if she had run into an invisible wall. The Cranes looked at Moe who moved slightly so he could swing the gun easily to cover them both.

"What's the big idea?" Riff asked, his voice uneven.

"Get that chain off!" Moe snapped. "Drop it on the floor, fast!"

This was a new Moe. The fat face had tightened: the black eyes were steady and threatening.

Riff hurriedly unwound the chain and let it drop.

"I was only fooling," he said, a whine in his voice. "What's eating you, Moe?"

"Get over there!" Moe snapped and jerked the gun towards Chita.

"You gone nuts or something?" Riff said, but he moved to join his sister.

Without taking his eyes off Riff, Moe bent and scooped up the chain.

"Now I'll ask the questions," he said. "What's going on here?"

There was a long pause, then Zelda who had been watching this scene, her eyes wide with fear, said breathlessly, "You mustn't hurt him! We are leaving together! He and I are getting married! If you will help us, I'll see my father gives you some money."

This news so stunned Moe that he lowered his gun to stare blankly at Zelda.

Quick to see his opportunity, Riff said, "That's the McCoy, Moe. We've taken a fancy to each other. Listen, this is a cinch. We'll take her back and her old man will be so pleased he won't sick the cops on to us. We'll be in the clear . . . the three of us. How's about it, pally? She and I will get married and we'll take care of you."

Moe looked at Zelda and he saw the way she was regarding Riff, then he looked at Chita and he realized that this was something she didn't go along with.

Moe thought of Kramer. He cursed himself for ever suggesting the Cranes should come in on this job. There were three more days before Kramer could collect the final ransom. He now had Zelda and Riff against him. What was he to do with them? Chita might be on his side, but he knew he couldn't trust her. Then he had the Dermott girl in his hair too.

It was while he was standing in the hot evening sunlight, trying to solve this problem that he saw a cloud of approaching dust: the unmistakable sign of an approaching car.

CHAPTER NINE

Tom Harper pulled up outside the five-barred gate that guarded the entrance to Wastelands.

As he got out of the car to open the gate, he wiped his sweating face. It was a hot evening, but he realized he was sweating more than he usually did. He was aware too of the uncomfortable feeling in the pit of his stomach: a feeling of fear.

He was unarmed, and he was about to drive up to this house which for the moment, he couldn't see and he was then going to ring on the front door bell. If his Chief was right, hidden in the house were dangerous hoods who had kidnapped one of the richest girls in the world. Unhappily, Harper thought, his Chief was invariably right. If these hoods got the slightest hint by some mistake he might make that he was a Federal Officer, they would kill him. Kidnappers had nothing to lose. The fact that they were kidnappers automatically put their lives in jeopardy. They wouldn't hesitate to kill him and then make a bolt for it.

Harper opened the gate, got in his car and drove up the drive. He drove slowly and his alert eyes took in the scene. He grimaced. The place offered no cover. There were a few small sand dunes behind which a man could hide, but they were too far away from the house. He could see as he drove that any car approaching would create a tell-tale dust cloud.

As he drove past the sand dunes, he saw the house. It was a quarter of a mile from him, set on a flat plane of sand, surrounded by green lawns and several outbuildings. He saw at once that there was no hope of approaching the house in daylight without being seen. He knew from the previous night that the moon shed a brilliant white light over the desert. It would be tricky and dangerous even to make the attempt at night.

He whistled through his teeth, thinking that Dennison

would have a job on his hands if he meant to rush the place.

As he drew nearer to the house, he could see the long, deserted veranda. He noticed all the windows were closed. It looked as if no one was at home. Then he noticed a Lincoln car parked near the house. It was dusty and had Californian number plates. He memorized the number as he pulled up near the car.

He felt instinctively that he was being watched. He got out of the car and stood for some moments regarding the house, then with casual strides and a thumping heart, he reached the veranda steps, mounted them and rang the front door bell.

As he waited, he thought ruefully that although Dennison was his future father-in-law, he certainly dreamed up some tough jobs for him.

There was a long pause, then the door opened and Chita regarded him, her face expressionless, one eyebrow lifted.

The sight of her gave Harper a jolt. Dennison had supplied him with the description of the girl who had been riding with Zelda Van Wylie just before Zelda's disappearance given to him by Patrol Officer Murphy. Harper recognized Chita at once from this description.

So Dennison was right as usual, he thought. I've walked right into them.

"Sorry to disturb," he said with a wide, friendly smile, "but I was passing. Could I see Mr. Dermott for a moment?" He inclined his head slightly to one side. "You wouldn't be Mrs. Dermott?"

"They're both out," Chita said in a cold, flat voice.

"Mr. Harris-Jones . . . in case you don't know he owns this place," Harper said. "He is renting it to me in a couple of months. As I was passing, I wondered if I could look the house over. I'm not all that sure if it will be big enough for my requirements."

"I can't let you in, while they're out."

Harper widened his smile which was beginning to make his face ache.

"I can see that. Well, then I'll get along. I shouldn't have bothered you, but . . ."

"Yeah," Chita said. "You told me: you happened to be passing," and she shut the door in his face.

Still aware that he was being watched, Harper walked to his car. The back of his neck felt prickly. He didn't hurry although he wanted to run. In spite of the fact that he kept wondering if he was going to get a bullet in his back, his eyes kept busy. There was a small cabin to his right, probably for the staff, to his left a double garage, then this expanse of lawn and another vast expanse of sand. It would be a hell of a place to approach without being seen.

It wasn't until he was in his car and driving fast down the drive-in that he began to relax. He had the information that Dennison wanted and he had got away with his skin in one piece: how Dennison was going to tackle this place happily was Dennisons's headache.

Once out of sight of the house, Harper pulled up and jotted down the number of the Lincoln. He then drove on fast to Pitt City. There he called Dennison.

"You hit it right on the nose," he told Dennison when he came on the line. "This girl who was driving with Miss Van Wylie came to the door. From the description, I'm certain it's the same girl." He went on to describe the approach to the ranch house and gave Dennison careful details of the layout of the house.

"Okay," Dennison said. "Here's what you do now. Take Brody and Letts and go back there after dark. Get as close to the place as you can . . . you'll have to walk part of the way. Take a pair of field glasses with you. I want a twenty-four hour non-stop watch kept on the house. Go prepared. I don't have to tell you what you want. Get Franklin of Pitt City to fit you out. I want to know who is in the house. Understand,"

"Yeah," Harper said.

"The one thing you have to take care about is that no one in the house has the slightest idea they are being watched. That's your responsibility. Take no risks. Good luck," and Dennison hung up.

The reception clerk of the Mount Crescent Hotel, Los Angeles, smiled politely as Vic Dermott came up to the desk.

"You have a reservation for me," Vic said. "The name's Jack Howard."

"That's right, Mr. Howard. Room 25. You will be staying only the one night."

"Yes." Vic was aware the clerk was staring curiously at his bruised face. "Just the one night."

He signed the register, handed his grip to the bell-hop and followed him to the elevator.

The time was twenty minutes to six. When the bell-hop had finally finished fussing around the bleak little room and had gone, Vic sat on the bed and rested his aching face in his hands. His thoughts were of Carrie and Junior. He wondered fearfully what was happening to them.

He had eight hundred thousand dollars in one hundred dollar bills in his suitcase. He had had no trouble in cashing the first two cheques. Tomorrow, he would buy another suitcase, and then go to the Chase National Bank and cash the third cheque. Then he would leave Los Angeles and drive up the coast as directed. At eleven o'clock tonight, this fat gangster had said he would telephone.

The nagging ache of his face and the nervous tension of the day exhausted him. He dropped back across the bed and closed his eyes. He hoped he would sleep for a while.

At the Rose Arms Hotel, San Francisco, Kramer poured himself a large whisky from the bottle standing on the dressing-table, added water and tried to make himself comfortable in the armchair that was a shade too small for his bulk.

He kept looking impatiently at his watch. The time now was five minutes to eleven. Had Dermott succeeded in picking up the first of the money? How were things going at Wastelands? Kramer drank some of the whisky. Maybe he had better ease off with this drinking, he thought. He had been drinking steadily since he had had the indifferent hotel dinner. His head felt hot and there was this goddam nagging pain in his side. He drank again, then set down the glass. He lit a cigar and then reached for the telephone. He asked the hotel operator to connect him with the Mount Crescent Hotel, Los Angeles. There was a slight delay, then he got the number.

He recognized Dermott's voice.

"You know who this is," he said. "How did it go? Careful how you talk. Did you run into any trouble?"

"No," Vic said.

"You have the first consignment?"

"Yes."

Kramer grinned. When it came to planning, he was still in there, beating the best of them!

"Fine. Tomorrow you go to Santa Barbara, and then on to Salinas. I've booked a room for you at the Cambria Hotel under the same name. I'll call you this time tomorrow."

"I understand." A slight pause, then Vic said anxiously, "I want to call my wife. May I do that?"

"I shouldn't if I were you," Kramer said heavily. "Not unless you want to annoy our friend. He doesn't like telephone calls," and he hung up.

He finished the whisky and refilled his glass. His heavy face was flushed and sweat beads made his thinning hair glisten in the hard overhead light.

He was now eight hundred thousand dollars to the good, he told himself. In another three days, he would have four million dollars in cash! There was Moe and these two young punks to take care of, but even after their cut had been deducted, he would still have three and a half million dollars for himself. At his age, that was lasting money!

He felt a sudden need to talk to Helene. He hesitated for some moments before he put the call through. There could be no danger, he assured himself. Why should there be? He gave his home number to the operator and replaced the receiver. He grinned to himself. Helene would be worrying herself stiff, he thought. Maybe now was the time to tell her about Solly Lucas. She would have to know sooner or later. If she started asking too many questions, he would always hang up on her, but she had better be warned: no use jumping the whole thing on her at once.

The telephone bell rang and he picked up the receiver.

"Hello?" Helene said. Her voice sounded far away and tense. "Who's that?"

"This is your lover," Kramer said and laughed. He was feeling fine and a little drunk.

"Oh, Jim! What's happening. Where are you?"

Joe Seesbruger, one of Dennison's men, who had tapped in on Kramer's line, gently pressed down the start button of the tape recorder connected to the line.

"How are you, honey?" Kramer was saying. "Are you lonely without me?"

"Jim! Two Federal Officers have been here! They were asking for you!"

Kramer felt as if someone had punched him violently under the heart.

Seesbruger was signalling to the telephone engineer.

Trace this call fast!" he whispered.

"What?" Kramer was saying. "What did they want?"

"They wanted to talk to you. Oh, Jim, I'm so worried! They know Moe has been here! This man, Inspector Dennison . . ."

Kramer nearly dropped the receiver.

"Dennison!"

"Yes. He said Moe hasn't a restaurant. He said Moe hadn't a dime to call his own. He – he said he hoped for your sake you weren't planning anything bad. Oh, Jim! You're not, are you?"

Kramer was scarcely listening. He wished now he hadn't had so much to drink. He couldn't think clearly. Dennison! One of the smartest Feds in the business and an old enemy of his! Dennison was a man he dare not underestimate!

"I'll call you back," he said hurriedly. "There's nothing to worry about. I've got to go now. Don't worry," and he hung up.

The telephone engineer said, "That's a call from the Rose Arms Hotel, 'Frisco."

Seesbruger grabbed the telephone and asked to be put through to the Federal Bureau, San Francisco.

Kramer was on his feet. What a mad fool he had been

to have called Helene! They had seen him with Moe and they had rightly decided he was planning something. He had been stupid enough to have imagined he could lose them, but with Dennison on the job, he hadn't lost them! Dennison would have tapped his home telephone line! By now they would know he was at this hotel! In a few minutes, they would be here! He was already struggling into his lightweight dust coat. His suitcase only contained a change and his toilet things. To hell with it! He wouldn't have time to settle his check before the Feds arrived. He had to get out fast!

Eleven minutes later, two Federal Officers hurried into the Rose Arms Hotel. They flashed their badges and showed the startled reception clerk Kramer's photograph.

"Seen this man?" one of them asked.

"Why, sure," the clerk said. "That's Mr. Mason. He went out only two minutes ago."

The two Federal Officers exchanged exasperated glances. The taller of the two, Bob Arlan, said, "Did Mr. Mason make any telephone calls this evening?"

"I wouldn't know," the clerk said, "but I can easily find out." He started towards a door that led to the switchboard. Arlan followed him.

The telephone operator, large-eyed to be questioned by a Federal Officer, gave Arlan the information he needed.

Dennison was about to go home when Arlan called him.

"Kramer just beat us to it," Arlan reported. "He had one other call besides the call to his home. Around eleven, he talked to someone staying at the Mount Crescent Hotel, Los Angeles."

"Okay," Dennison said. "Forget Kramer now. I'm not ready to pick him up." He cut the connection and then got on to Seesbruger. "Stay where you are. I want details of every call put through to Mrs. Kramer."

Seesbruger said wearily he would stay right on the job.

Dennison looked at his watch. The time was ten minutes after midnight. He called home and warned his wife he would be late, then he went down to where he had parked his car and headed fast towards Los Angeles.

They were all in Carrie's bedroom which was unbearably hot because Moe had shut the windows when he had seen Harper approaching.

Carrie stood near the cot. Happily, Junior, overcome by the heat, was asleep. Zelda and Riff stood by the window, concealed by the net curtains. Moe, gun in hand, was in a position where he could see out of the window and yet watch the other three in the room.

They watched Harper get in his car and drive away. The door had been left ajar and they had all listened to the conversation between Chita and Harper. Now, Chita came back into the room.

"Okay," Moe said, relaxing a little. "Just one of those things. Get those windows open."

Riff pushed open the windows and let in the light evening breeze.

Moe said, "Listen you two. I don't give a damn what you all do after we've got the ransom. You can marry this girl or her grandmother for all I care, but you're not leaving here until Kramer comes back with the ransom. I've handled punks like you most of my life. If you think you can do something about it, try, but I warn you the next time you try to start something, I'm shooting first and crying over you after. That understood?"

Riff eyed him. He was seething with fury, but the way Moe had produced the gun as if by magic had chilled him. He knew he hadn't the equipment to go up against a man who could draw a gun that fast. He had no guts for a showdown with Moe.

"You're crazy in the head!" he snarled. "Can't you see this lets us out? We take her back and we're in the clear. We take the ransom and we're in trouble. Can't you see that, you stupid Wop?"

"No one's getting into trouble," Moe said quietly. "It's all been worked out. You two . . ." he waved his gun at the

Cranes, "keep out of here. From now on, you're going to live in the cabin over there. She . . ." he waved his gun at Zelda, "is staying right here. If either of you come within fifty yards of the house, you'll get a bullet. I won't kill you, but you'll get a broken leg. Got it?"

Riff grinned evilly at him.

"And what are you going to do, Wop?" he sneered. "Keep awake for three nights?"

The room shook with the bang of the gun. The vicious yellow flame that lit the shadows like a photographer's flash gun made Zelda scream.

Riff staggered back. His hand went to his ear. Blood showed on his fingers. Blood began to run down the side of his neck. Riff stared at his blood-stained fingers as if he couldn't believe his eyes.

Moe watched him. A faint whisp of smoke drifted from the gun barrel.

"I can shoot, Riff," he said softly. "Now get the hell out of here and stay out! You too!" to Chita.

Shocked and bleeding, Riff went out of the room. He was now holding a dirty handkerchief to his ear. The bullet had flicked off the lobe of his ear with the precision of a surgeon's knife.

As Chita followed him, Junior began to cry. Zelda had flung herself face down on the bed, sobbing and pounding the bed with her clenched fists. Carrie, white-faced from the shock of the exploding gun, picked Junior out of his cot.

Moe stood by the open window and watched Riff and Chita cross the expanse of green lawn until they reached the cabin and went inside, then he turned and looked at Carrie.

"You've got to watch this girl," he said gently. "Don't let her out of your sight. I'll watch the other two. They're bad. If you and your bambino want to get out of this alive, you'll have to work with me. We have three days before the ransom arrives." He paused, then said, "Are you going to be on my side?"

Carrie hesitated. So far this fat, swarthy Italian had behaved like a human being, she reasoned. The Cranes and this stupid girl were people she couldn't possibly trust. She realized she couldn't remain neutral in this nightmare affair. She had to take sides and there was no choice. She nodded slowly.

"Yes," she said. "I'll be on your side."

Moe visibly relaxed. He put his gun away. He stared at Junior who was still crying and Moe smiled.

"My brother had ten children," he said. "He was killed in the war. I looked after his kids. I'm good with babies. Could I have him?"

Carrie felt a cold shiver run down her spine. She began to refuse but there was this odd, kindly look in Moe's eyes that stopped her.

"He – he doesn't like strangers," she said. "Perhaps you . . ."

But Moe reached out and reluctantly she let him take the baby. The gangster and the baby stared at each other. Then Junior suddenly stopped bawling and screwed up his face as he continued to peer at Moe. Moe blew out his fat cheeks. He made a soft whistling noise, stopped, started the noise again and then grinned widely. Junior considered this, decided it was pretty funny and began to laugh.

Realizing no one was paying any attention to her hysterics, Zelda stopped crying and turned over. She glared at Moe and Carrie who continued to pay no attention to her.

"I like babies," Moe said. "They like me." He put Junior back into Carrie's arms and walked to the door. "You and me and the bambino together, huh? You watch her. If she gets troublesome, call me. I'll slap her."

He went out on to the verandah and sat down. From where he sat he could see the cabin and he could watch the windows that led out on to the veranda. He felt very uneasy. He was pretty sure he could trust Carrie, but the Cranes were like snakes. He couldn't remain awake for three nights. Riff had put his finger right on the weak spot of Moe's plans. He could only hope that Kramer would telephone and he could alert him to what was happening. Maybe Kramer would send someone or come himself. He looked across at the cabin. The shutters were closed. The door too was closed. He wondered what the Cranes were doing in there.

In the cabin, Riff was bent over the toilet basin, sopping cold water on his ear and cursing. The experience of being shot at had unnerved him.

Chita lolled in an armchair in the small sitting-room. From where she sat she could watch her brother. She made no effort to help him.

"Can't you do something?" Riff snarled as the blood continued to drip into the basin. "Don't just sit there! Can't you stop this bleeding?"

Chita didn't say anything. For the first time in her life she had no desire to help her brother. That he should have even contemplated marrying this rich little bitch had raised such a hatred and jealousy in her that she felt that the binding link that had always held them together had been severed with the force of an executioner's axe.

She knew Riff as she knew herself. She knew that when he had said he was going to marry Zelda that this was no cynical lie: he really meant to marry the girl. Already, he was planning how he would live on her money, how he was going to quit the rut of their tough, drab lives that Chita so much enjoyed. How he was going to wallow in the softness of riches. Chita knew that sooner or later he would drop her. He wouldn't want her continually tagging along. She would be in the way. He would give her money . . . she was sure he would do that, but he would want to be rid of her to absorb himself into the soft, futile, aimless life of the rich that would sap the guts out of him and he would become just another of the hundreds of playboys Chita had bedded with: spineless, gutless and useless.

Still cursing, Riff went into the bedroom, tore a strip off one of the sheets, made a pad and fixed it to his ear. He tied another strip of sheet around his head and finally stopped the flow of blood.

By the time he had finished, it was growing dark. He came into the sitting-room, his leather jacket bloodstained, his face pale, his eyes vicious with fury.

"What's eating you?" he snarled. "Couldn't you have helped me?"

Chita said nothing. She stared down at her long, slender legs, her face expressionless.

"That Wop!" Riff exploded. "Who'd have imagined he could shoot like that! He could have killed me!"

He might just as well be talking to himself for all the notice Chita took of him.

He stared at her for a long moment, feeling uneasy. She had never behaved this way to him before. Then because his pride wouldn't allow him to persuade her to talk to him, he went over to the window. He peered through the slits in the shutter. He could see Moe sitting on the veranda. If he had a gun, he could have picked Moe off. The range was nothing. From where he was standing, he couldn't have missed Moe. Then suddenly he remembered the mystery of the missing gun. He had put Dermott's gun in the hip pocket of his trousers. When he had gone to fetch the gun . . . it had gone! Someone must have taken it! It wasn't Moe because Moe hadn't been in the ranch house at the time the gun disappeared. So it had to be one of the three women who had taken it.

He turned and stared suspiciously at Chita who was lighting a cigarette.

"Did you take my gun?" he demanded.

She looked indifferently at him, her eyes cold and hostile. "Gun? What gun?"

Well, at least she was now talking to him, Riff thought.

"Dermott's gun!" he snarled. "I had it in my pants pocket. It's gone!"

"What do you expect if you're in such a hurry to throw off your pants?" Chita said with a sneer.

"Did you take it?" Riff shouted, his face darkening with fury.

"Why should I take it?" Chita got to her feet. "I'm hungry." She started to cross the sitting-room towards the tiny kitchen.

Riff grabbed her arm.

"Did you take it?" he yelled.

She threw his hand off with a strength that always surprised him.

"Keep your paws off me! I haven't got it! I don't care who's got it!"

She went into the kitchen and he heard her open the door of the refrigerator.

He went back to the window, cursing and worried. He continued to stare through the shutter at Moe.

It was a little after one o'clock in the morning when Dennison walked into the reception lobby of the Mount Crescent Hotel, Los Angeles.

The day clerk was about to go home. Dennison was lucky. Usually, the day clerk left much earlier than this, but it so happened his girl friend had stood him up and because he didn't want to return alone to his dismal bed-sitter, he had hung around the hotel talking to the night clerk.

Dennison identified himself, then he asked about the new arrivals at the hotel. The clerk showed him the register. After some talk, Dennison said, "and this guy, Jack Howard ... remember him?"

"Why, sure," the clerk said. "He's tall, dark and well-dressed. He has a bad bruise on the left side of his face . . . a hell of a bruise."

Dennison grunted.

"Let me have a pass key," he said. "He's the guy I want to talk to."

The clerk hesitated, then went around the counter, took a key off a hook and handed it to Dennison.

"We don't want any trouble here, Inspector," he said without much hope. "You'll know that."

"Sure, sure," Dennison said. "Who wants trouble?"

Vic had been unable to sleep. He lay in the darkness, thinking of Carrie. He had been lying, worrying for the past two hours. He kept trying to assure himself that so long as he carried out his part of the bargain. Carrie and Junior would be safe, but he couldn't get the image of the Cranes out of his mind. Those two really scared him. They were capable of anything. Suddenly, he heard a faint sound that brought him alert, his heart thumping.

Dennison had gently pushed the door key out of the lock. The key fell to the floor. He then inserted the pass key, turned it and opened the door. As he did so, Vic snapped on the light.

The two men looked at each other. Dennison came in and shut the door.

"Inspector Dennison," he said. "Federal Bureau. You're Mr. Victor Dermott, I believe?"

Vic hesitated, then he said, "That's my name." He sat up in bed. "Just what is all this? Why have you . . . ?"

"It's all right, Mr. Dermott," Dennison said with his fatherly smile he kept for special occasions. "I'm here to help you. We know what's going on." He sat on the bed. "We know the spot you're in. Now look, let's co-operate. We want to catch these thugs, but at the same time, we don't want to cause any trouble for Mrs. Dermott and your baby. I give you my word we won't make any move until the ransom is paid and Mrs. Dermott is freed. Maybe it will give you some assurance to know I have three of my men watching Wastelands right now. If anything bad should start, they'll be within reach where they will help your wife."

Vic felt cold, and there was a sick fear growing in him.

"Why couldn't you have kept out of this?" he said angrily. "What's four million dollars to a man like Van Wylie? These devils are deadly! They won't hesitate to kill everyone in the house! They've already murdered my servant. They . . ."

"Just a moment," Dennison broke in sharply. "You said they've killed your servant?"

Vic pulled himself together.

"I'm not absolutely sure, but there was blood in the cabin where my servant sleeps. He's disappeared."

"They could have hit him hard the way you were hit," Dennison said soothingly. "Now look, Mr. Dermott, try to relax. I would feel the same way if I were in your position, but you mustn't get too excited. No one knows you and I are meeting. Right now, all I want from you is information. I want a description of these people. I give you my word we won't make a move until your wife and baby are safe. We won't even make a move without your approval."

Vic lay back. His face still ached. He remembered Kramer's warning.

"I can't tell you a thing," he said. "I'm not interested in anything except keeping my wife and baby safe."

"That I can understand," Dennison said, "but this goes further than that, Mr. Dermott. I want you to trust me. Suppose I ask questions and you tell me if I'm right?" He smiled, then went on, "The man we think is behind this kidnapping is around sixty, tall, heavily built and with a whisky complexion. Right?"

Vic hesitated, shrugged then nodded.

"He has another guy working with him: an Italian; short, fat and swarthy. Right?"

Again Vic nodded.

"There's a girl: dyed blonde, tall, good-looking in a coarse way, around twenty-two or three. Right?"

Again Vic nodded.

"Then there's another of them, but I haven't got him tagged," Dennison said. "He's the one who interests me."

Again Vic hesitated, then he said, "He's the girl's twin. He's the one who scares me . . . a vicious, brutal thug. He's the one who hit me. He binds his fist with a bicycle chain."

"Describe him," Dennison said.

Vic gave him a description of Riff and when he was finished, Dennison got to his feet.

"You carry on the way you're going now, Mr. Dermott," he said. "Get the ransom." He put a card on the bedside table. "That's my telephone number. Memorize it and then destroy the card. When you have the ransom, telephone me. These hoods imagine once they have the ransom, they are in the clear, but they have badly underestimated Van Wylie. As soon as we know your wife and baby and Miss Van Wylie are safe, we're going after them. From now on, three of my best men will be tailing you. If you want help at any time, they'll be right with you. You have nothing to worry about.

You have my word we won't make a move until your wife is safe."

Vic shrugged helplessly.

"I guess I have to rely on you," he said, "but please hold off until these thugs have left Wastelands."

"You have my word," Dennison said and moved to the door. "There's nothing to worry about. I'm sorry to have walked in like that. Good night, Mr. Dermott," and he left the room.

Vic lay still, staring bleakly at the opposite wall while he listened to Dennison's heavy tread diminishing down the corridor.

CHAPTER TEN

CAUTIOUSLY, Zelda lifted her head and looked across the room to where Carrie was sleeping. Light came from the brilliant desert moon, seeping through the slits in the shutters and for some moments Zelda watched Carrie. Then with infinite care, she pushed aside the sheet and sat up. She waited, scarcely breathing, then she swung her feet to the floor.

Silence brooded over the ranch house. Zelda made no further move for some moments. She sat on the edge of the bed, trying to make up her mind whether to take the risk of creeping out of the ranch house and over to the cabin or to return to bed. She didn't know if the fat Italian was awake. She thought it was probable by now he was sleeping, but she couldn't be sure.

She burned for Riff. If she could reach him, she had no doubt that he could get her away from this place. She had to reach him!

She stood up. Motionless, her heart thumping, she stared at Carrie, but as Carrie made no movement, she picked up the shirt and trousers she had left on a chair by the bed. Very cautiously, she slipped into the trousers, dropped her night-dress on the bed, then put on the shirt.

Carrie moved in her sleep and Zelda froze, her heart fluttering. She waited, then as Carrie went on sleeping, Zelda moved silently on bare feet to the door. She eased it open and stepped out into the lobby. There she stood for some moments, listening. Satisfied there was no sound to alarm her, she crept across to the kitchen, eased open the back door and stepped out into the hot moonlit night.

Around the front of the house, Moe had struggled to keep awake, but he wasn't made for the endurance of a sleepless night. He had relaxed in the comfortable bamboo chair, his gun held in his lap, and within an hour he had dozed off. Now he was sleeping heavily.

Zelda skirted the house, paused long enough to hear

Moe's soft snoring, then she ran across the lawn, across the sandy drive to the cabin.

In the cabin, Chita had taken over the bedroom and had shut herself in. She lay restlessly on the bed, half dozing, half awake. In the sitting-room, Riff too was dozing. He had spent two long hours watching the ranch house, but as the moon moved and shadows closed in around the house he was unable to see Moe. He now had no idea if Moe was awake or asleep. He hadn't the nerve to go out there. His ear ached. He wasn't chancing a bullet in the leg. Now, stretched out on two chairs, he dozed and thought of his future with Zelda.

A slight sound alerted Chita. She sat up to listen. A door creaked, then she heard soft whispering coming from the sitting-room. She got off the bed and moved silently to the door. She listened, her ear pressed against the door panel. She recognized Zelda's voice. A hot rush of blood went through her. Carefully, slowly and patiently, she eased back the door handle and gently opened the door no more than an inch so she could hear and yet not be seen.

As the front door of the cabin creaked open, Riff started up, but relaxed when he heard Zelda whisper, "It's all right, Riff . . . it's me."

She came through the darkness of the room and knelt beside him, her arms going around him, her head against his chest.

"I couldn't keep away," she said, her fingers moving through his close-cut hair, careful to avoid his hurt ear. "Are you badly hurt?"

"Where is he?" Riff asked, his thick blunt fingers against her back, pulling her to him. "Is he asleep?"

"Yes." She moaned softly at the hard, brutal touch of his hands. "Oh, Riff! Can't we get away? Can't we go now?"

Riff could see the bright moonlight coming through the shutters. If he went out there now and Moe woke up, Moe could pick him off like a sitting rabbit.

"This Wop can shoot," he said. "We'll have to wait. There's time. You saw what he did to me." He was speaking in a voice scarcely above a whisper.

"Where is she?" Zelda whispered, her arms tightening around him.

"In the other room . . . asleep. Keep your voice down. She mustn't hear us." He got to his feet, pulling her against him. They stood in the darkness, straining against each other.

Chita shut the door and went back to the bed and sat on it, her hands into fists gripped tightly between her knees. She listened to the faint sounds that came through the panels of the door. Finally, as these sounds became more out of control, she got to her feet. She stood hesitating. There was one way to stop this thing going any further: one way to keep her brother for herself. She heard Zelda stifle a cry of pleasure and pain and that decided her. She crossed to the window, and opened the shutters. She looked across at the ranch house, then she climbed out of the window and closed the shutters after her.

Moving silently, she slid around the cabin, keeping in the shadows. There was one patch of moonlight between the cabin and the garage. This she ran through and paused in the shadow of the garage door. She looked back and listened. No one shouted: no one moved. Cautiously, she lifted the swing-up door to the garage, moved into the darkness and then shut the door after her. For some moments she groped impatiently for the light switch, found it and turned it down. She blinked around the garage where the Cadillac and the estate wagon stood, side by side. At the far end of the garage, she found what she was looking for: a long-handled shovel used often enough when the wind caused the sand to form into drifts.

She picked up the shovel, turned off the light, opened the garage door and walked out into the open.

It took her the best part of two hours to find and open Di-Long's grave. Riff had indicated vaguely where he had buried the Vietnamese, and Chita had to make several false starts before she finally located where the body lay under the sand. By then it was some time after two o'clock and the moon had climbed high, shedding its hard light over the ranch house.

Moe continued to snore softly. Carrie was dreaming of Vic. Riff and Zelda, exhausted, lay on the floor, half sleeping, half awake.

A quarter of a mile from the ranch house, Tom Harper with Letts and Brody, lay at the base of the nearest sand dune to the house. Harper had borrowed a periscope from the 'Frisco Field Agency. This he had erected so that he could watch the ranch house without being seen. Letts and Brody were asleep. Harper had been keeping close watch on the house, but he had failed to see Chita leave the cabin. The periscope wasn't much use in the hours of darkness.

Chita regained the bedroom without being seen or heard. She lay down on the bed. The hatred for her brother and for Zelda gnawed at her. She listened to the continual whispering that came to her from the other room. The sound was like salt in a wound in her body.

Satiated and now bored with Zelda, Riff finally moved away from her.

"You'd better get back," he said and sat up. "Come on! Get your hands off me!" Brutally, he shoved her away. "Get moving! It'll be light in an hour."

Reluctantly, Zelda got to her feet and began to dress.

"Aren't we getting out of here?" she asked. "I thought . . ."

"Keep your voice down!" Riff hissed.

"But aren't we leaving?" she whispered as she pulled up the zip on her trousers.

"Do you want a hole in your skin?" Riff said. He was sick of her now. He had exhausted his lust on her and now he wanted to be rid of her. "That Wop will shoot . . . and he can shoot!"

"But, darling, you're not scared of a fat little man like that?" Zelda said, staring at him.

"Him? Who'd be scared of a punk like him? But I don't go for the gun . . . he can shoot. Look, get the hell out of here!" Riff waved to the door. "I'll fix something! You leave me to handle it . . . go on, beat it!"

No man had ever talked this way to Zelda. She found it exciting.

"You do love me, don't you?" she said and moved towards him.

"Sure, sure, sure." Riff was nearly frantic with impatience. "Now get going."

He took her by her arm and shoved her to the door, opening it and shoving her roughly out into the twilight of the desert.

Propelled by his violent push, Zelda half ran, half staggered down the wooden slope leading from the cabin. Then she stopped short and stared at the awful thing that lay at her feet. She stared, as Riff was staring, then she put her fingers into her hair and began to scream.

Chita listened to the screams with sadistic relish.

At the Cambria Hotel, Salinas, Kramer asked the telephone operator to connect him to a Paradise City number. He was calling Phil Baker, the man with whom he played regular golf and who was the only person Kramer could think of right at this minute whom he could rely on as a friend.

Kramer had decided to move into the Cambria Hotel where Vic Dermott was to come later in the day. Kramer was losing his nerve. The fact that Dennison was taking an interest in his affairs upset him. Dennison was the last man Kramer wanted to be poking his nose into what he was doing. Kramer now began to wonder if he shouldn't take what money Dermott had already collected and clear the hell out of the country. By now, Dermott should have a million and a half dollars in cash. Kramer was trying to make up his mind whether to take the money and disappear and leave Zegetti and the Cranes to whistle for their share or go through with the original plan. He felt he just had to talk to Helene before he finally decided.

Baker came on the line. The time was a little after five o'clock in the afternoon.

"Phil . . . this is Jim," Kramer said. "Something has blown up. Look, I'm relying on you as a friend. I want you to do something for me and I don't want you to ask questions. Will you do it for me?"

Obviously puzzled, Baker asked, "Where have you been? I missed a game because I waited for you."

"I'm sorry, but I've got into a situation that needs a little handling," Kramer said impatiently. "Will you do something for me? I want you to do it without a lot of questions."

"Why, sure, Jim . . . anything." Baker sounded now a little hurt. "What can I do?"

"Will you go out to my house and tell Helene to go to the club and telephone me at seven o'clock sharp? Will you do that for me?"

"Of course," Baker said. "But I don't get it. Why don't you . . . ?"

"I said no questions!" Kramer barked. "Will you or won't you do this for me?"

"I said I would, didn't I? You want me to see Helene and tell her to go to the club and call you at seven: right?"

"That's it."

Kramer gave him the telephone number of the hotel.

"When I see you next week, I'll explain, but right now, this is something I don't want to go into. Okay, Phil?"

"Sure . . . I'll get over to your place in half an hour. You leave it to me." There was a pause, then Baker said, "Jim . . . you're not in any trouble?"

"For God's sake, Phil! Do what I'm asking you," Kramer snarled. "I'll tell you about it next time we meet. So long for now," and he hung up.

He sat, staring blankly out of the window, waiting. It was an interminable wait, but finally a few minutes to seven o'clock, Helene called him.

"Hi, lover," Kramer said, forcing himself to sound gay. "How are things? Are you all right?"

There was a pause, then Helene said in a voice Kramer scarcely recognized, "Am I all right? How can you say such a thing? What's happening? Jim! What's going on? I have a right to know! Phil came out here . . . he looked at me as if I were some kind of a criminal. What is happening?"

Kramer felt a shooting pain in his left side as he said, "Relax, Helene. I want to talk to you without the Feds listening in. Don't you realize that they have tapped our line?"

"Why should they have tapped our line?" Helene demanded, her voice strident. "Why should they? Have you done something wrong? I don't know what you are talking about!"

Kramer moved restlessly in his chair. This was going to be tricky, he thought angrily. He had never heard Helene talk this way before.

"Skip it, Helene," he said roughly. "I want to see you. The Feds will be tailing you. You'll have to lose them. You did it in the past: you can do it now. When you have lost them, I want you to come to the Cambria Hotel at Salinas. I'm staying here. Could be you and I are going on a long trip . . . could be, we're going to lose ourselves."

There was a long silence over the line and Kramer got more irritated.

"Helene!"

"I'm here. So you are in trouble." Her voice had a note of despair that sent a chill through Kramer. "With all your money . . . how could you be so stupid?"

"Don't call me stupid!" Kramer exclaimed, outraged that his wife should say such a thing to him. "You don't know the half of it! Solly took all our money! The thieving son-of-a-bitch gambled the lot away . . . four million dollars! He stripped us clean!"

"Solly?" Helene's voice shot up. "Oh, no! Solly wouldn't do that to us? How could he?"

"Well, he did! But I'm getting the money back. Listen, Helene, you come out here and I'll explain everything. For Pete's sake, be careful how you come. You've got to lose whoever is tailing you . . be sure you do that. Don't lead him to me here . . . do you understand?"

Again there was a long pause and Kramer, his face red, the pain in his side making him sweat, said "Helene! Are you still there?"

"Yes. I was thinking. So we haven't any more money?"

"That's it, but we will have. I'm working on a scheme

that'll bring us in as much as we've lost. You come out here and I'll explain what's been happening."

"No, Jim. I'm sorry, but I'm not coming. I'm getting old now. You're old too, Jim . . . far too old to move back into the rackets again. Come home. We'll work this thing out together. I'm not going to try to dodge Federal Officers at my time of life. Maybe it was fun fifteen years ago, but it won't be fun now. Come home, Jim. We'll work something out together."

"We haven't any home," Kramer said furiously. "Don't you listen to what I'm telling you? We are stripped clean! I'm in something that will get us back as we were, but you have to come out here and join up with me. Now come on, but be very careful how you come."

"I'm not coming," Helene said. "Years ago, we went through all this, but I'm not going through it now. I thought and hoped you and I were free of the rackets. I'm not coming. Goodbye, Jim. I'll manage somehow and I hope you will also manage. If you change your mind, if you drop whatever you're doing, then I'll be waiting, but otherwise, Jim, it's goodbye."

The distinct click over the line as she hung up was like the slamming of a door that had, up to this moment, led into a few years of life that Kramer had enjoyed and had been proud of.

He jiggled the cross-bar of the telephone, unable to believe that his wife had actually hung up on him. Helene! A second-rate singer he had rescued from a third-rate night club . . . to have done such a thing to him! A woman to whom he had given wealth, position and social security! He couldn't believe it!

Slowly, he replaced the receiver. He looked around the small, bleak room. He sat there for some time, sweating, a little frightened and in pain.

"Goodbye, Jim," she had said.

There had been a final, I'm-finished-with-you note in her voice.

Slowly, Kramer got to his feet. He walked with heavy, plodding steps to his suitcase and took from it a bottle of whisky. He went into the bathroom and poured himself a stiff shot. He drank it without water, refilled the glass and then walked slowly back into the bedroom.

Helene! What would she do? There would be no money in the house. He thought of the mink stole he had promised her. What the hell did she imagine she was going to do without him?

The telephone bell rang, startling him so that he slopped whisky on the carpet. He put down the glass and picked up the telephone receiver.

"You asked to be told when Mr. Jack Howard arrived," the reception clerk said. "He's just booked in: Room 135."

"Thanks," Kramer said and hung up. He finished his drink and lit a cigar. Room 135 would be on his floor: down the far end of the corridor. Dermott would have a million and a half in cash. What was he going to do? Kramer asked himself. Could he really believe that Helene had said goodbye? If she meant it, then why should he stick around here? Why not take what there was of the ransom and get the hell out of here? Why should he bother his head about Moe and the Cranes?

The cigar tasted bitter, and with an impatient gesture, he stubbed it out.

A man could live pretty well with a million and a half dollars. He could get on a boat and go to Cuba. Maybe, later, Helene would join him. He closed his eyes. He felt curiously tired and the nagging pain in his side worried him. Could he walk out on Moe? He ran his thick fingers through his hair as he tried to decide what he was to do. Finally, still undecided, he hoisted himself to his feet, took another drink and then walked out into the long corridor. He started down towards Room 135.

Vic Dermott was washing his hands in the small bathroom when he heard a knock on the door. Drying his hands, he crossed the room and still holding the towel, he turned the key in the lock and opened the door. The sight of Kramer startled him. He backed away as Kramer came in, pushing the door shut behind him.

"Well?" Kramer said. "How have you been making out?"

"All right," Vic said and tossed the towel on to the bed. "I didn't expect to see you here."

"How much money have you got?" Kramer said.

"A million, six hundred thousand so far," Vic said and waved to the two suitcases lying on the floor near his bed.

"Let's see . . . open them up," Kramer said.

"Help yourself," Vic said quietly.

Kramer stared for a long, threatening moment at Vic who stared back at him, then with a grunt, he went over to the suitcases, bent and opened one of them. As he did so, he felt something that was like a red-hot spear drive through his body. His big hands had already lifted the lid of the suitcase. He fell forward, his eyes staring at the mass of one hundred dollar bills in the case, the pain in his side making him speechless.

He tried to say something. He tried to get his face away from the open suitcase. He was suddenly without strength, like a punctured sawdust doll. Then there was another shocking jolt of pain that made him groan and he relaxed into death, his hands grasping at the money he would never spend.

Paralysed with surprise and shock, Vic watched the big man die. It was only when the heavy body sprawled on the floor that Vic moved forward in a helpless, hopeless attempt to do something.

He stood over the dead body and he thought of Carrie and Junior. He remembered suddenly that the Federal Officer had said someone would be near him all the time. He went to the door and opened it, then moved out into the corridor. There was a long pause, then a door opened further down the corridor and a tall, powerfully-built man appeared. He looked at Vic and raised his eyebrows.

"You'd better come," Vic said. "He's dead."

An hour later, Jay Dennison arrived at the hotel. He went immediately to Vic's room. Vic had been waiting in Kramer's room with Abe Mason, the Federal Officer. They now both joined Dennison who stared down at Kramer's body while he rubbed his jaw thoughtfully. Then he looked at the two suitcases packed with money.

"How much is there in that little lot?" he asked.

Vic told him.

Dennison turned to Mason.

"Fix it to get the body removed when the hotel is asleep," he said. "I don't want any publicity about this." He closed the suitcases and picked them up. "Let's you and me, Mr. Dermott, go somewhere where we can talk."

Vic led the way back to Kramer's room and the two men shut themselves in. Dennison sat on the bed while Vic sat in the only armchair.

"You have enough money here to satisfy the other three," Dennison said. "I guess we'd better start things moving. I want you to return to Wastelands and give these hoods this money. Once they get it, they'll quit. Once away from Wastelands, they'll be out in the open. My men will close in on them and that'll be their finish. Would you like a gun, Mr. Dermott?"

Vic shook his head.

"No ... if I go back there alone, they are certain to search me. If they find a gun on me, they'll know something is up. No: I don't want a gun."

"We could hide one in your car."

Vic shook his head.

"I'm taking no chances. This is too important to my wife and myself. Besides, I'm hopeless with a gun."

"Well, okay: maybe you're right." Dennison thought for a long moment. "They'll want to know where Kramer is. Tell them he is waiting for them at the Arrowhead Motel: Cabin 57. They'll never get as far as the motel, but it'll sound right."

"You think so?" Vic was doubtful. "Suppose one of them telephones the motel and asks for Kramer?"

Dennison smiled.

"I'll fix all that, Mr. Dermott. The owner of the motel has worked with me before now. He'll say Kramer has gone out."

"I have still more cheques to cash. What do I do with them?"

"It's my bet Kramer hasn't told the others how much he was asking. They'll be happy enough with a million and half dollars. Let me have the rest of the cheques. I'll return them to Mr. Van Wylie."

As Vic handed over the remaining cheques, he said, "They don't expect me back for another two days. Won't they be suspicious when I turn up so soon?"

"Tell them Kramer speeded up the operation," Dennison returned. "Tell them as you had no trouble cashing the cheques you got way ahead of schedule. Why should they care?"

Vic thought about all this. He didn't like it, but he couldn't see what else to do.

"All right: then I'm ready to go."

Dennison looked at his watch.

"You can get to San Bernardino in three or four hours. Stay the night there and get to Wastelands around ten o'clock tomorrow morning. I have three of my men staked out in the sand dunes, watching the house. You won't be alone, but play it carefully. It's my bet when these three get their hands on all this money, they'll quit and quit fast."

"I'm not waiting until tomorrow morning," Vic said with quiet determination. "I don't intend to leave my wife out there for another night. I'm driving to Wastelands tonight."

"Now look, Mr. Dermott . . ." Dennison began, but Vic cut him short.

"I said I'm driving to Wastelands tonight. And no one is going to stop me!"

Dennison studied him, then shrugged.

"I guess I'd act the same way. Okay, but watch it."

As Vic picked up the two suitcases, Dennison reached for the telephone.

Harper was about to shake Letts awake to take over the watch on the ranch house when he heard Zelda's screams.

The sound woke the other two Federal Officers and the three men looked anxiously at one another.

"What the hell's going on up there?" Letts said, getting to his feet.

The screams that came shrilly through the still night air suddenly stopped and silence once again descended over the desert.

"I'm going up there," Harper said.

"Wait," Letts said. "I'm better at this kind of caper than you. I could get up there without being seen. If they spot us, the balloon will go up."

Letts was a small, wiry man who had seen service as a jungle scout during the war. Harper recognized his claim. If anyone could get to the ranch house without being seen, it would be Letts.

"Okay, Alex, but get up there fast. I want to know what's going on."

As Letts moved forward, first on hands and knees and then flat in the sand, Harper got on to the two-way radio and tried to contact Dennison. He was told Dennison wasn't available.

"Find him!" Harper said urgently. "There's trouble up here. A woman has been screaming. Find and tell him!"

At the sound of Zelda's screams, Moe came out of his heavy sleep with a start that brought him unsteadily to his feet. For a long moment he couldn't recollect where he was. He had hold of his gun, his breathing was heavy, his heart pounding, then he came fully awake and looked across to the cabin where he could see Zelda, her hands in her hair, screaming.

Riff ran to her and slapped her face. Her screams cut off. Sobbing frantically, she tried to cling to him, but he shoved her away.

The stench of death from the Vietnamese sickened both of them.

Slowly, Moe came down the veranda steps. A light had come up in Carrie's room, and Carrie peered fearfully out of the open window. Even from where she was, the smell of death came to her.

Zelda turned and ran blindly down the drive. Riff started after her, then stopped when he saw Moe coming towards him, gun in hand.

Moe yelled after Zelda, but she kept on running.

"Get after her!" he shouted to Riff. "She's getting away!"

But Riff paid no attention. He was now staring at the man he had killed. Fury, frustration and fear surged through him. He suddenly realized he would never marry Zelda and his hopes for a rich, easy life now exploded in his face.

Then Moe saw the body of the Vietnamese and he stopped short, feeling the hairs on the nape of his neck lift.

Chita had slid off the bed. She was watching gleefully through the slit in the shutter.

Letts, a hundred yards away, found himself right out in the open. In the hard light of the moon, he realized if he now made a movement forward, he must be seen. He watched Moe and Riff standing over something dark, lying in the sand. He then saw Zelda running frantically towards him. He recognized her, and on impulse, he jumped to his feet.

"I'm a Federal Officer," he said, catching hold of her arm, bringing her to an abrupt stop. "Keep going . . . there's . . ."

Moe suddenly saw Letts rise out of the ground. He saw Zelda jump clear of him and run on. He fired at Letts. He had no intention of pulling the trigger. This was an instinctive movement brought on by shock and fear.

Shot through the head, Letts pitched forward as the gun flash made Riff start back. By now Zelda had disappeared beyond the first of the sand dunes.

Both Riff and Moe remained motionless, staring at the body lying in the sand.

"What's happening?" Moe quavered. He felt he was going out of his mind. "What's going on?"

Cursing, Riff ran to where Letts lay. He bent over him, turned him and began pawing at his body. He found Letts's wallet and then the F.B.I. badge. He peered at the badge, then scrambling to his feet, he raced back to Moe.

"It's a Fed!" he snarled as he reached Moe. "You stupid jerk! You've killed him!"

As Zelda blundered on down the drive, Harper, seeing her come, jumped up and grabbed her.

"It's alright. We're Federal Officers," he said and clamped his hand over her mouth to stop her screaming. She wrestled with him, her eyes wide with terror and shock, but he finally quieted her by repeating over and over again that he was a Federal Officer. She went suddenly limp and collapsed against him.

"Jack!" Harper said urgently. "Get her to Dennison! It's Miss Van Wylie!"

Brody was looking towards the ranch house.

"How's about the woman and child up there?"

"Do what I say!" Harper snapped. "I'll take care of them."

Brody caught hold of Zelda and half dragging, half supporting her, took her to the jeep, hidden behind a big sand dune.

Harper turned his attention to the ranch house. He saw three figures running towards the house. They disappeared inside. From where he stood, he heard the door slam. The light in one of the rooms went out.

As the jeep started up, he, and Brody in the jeep, saw the lights of an approaching car. Zelda was sobbing hysterically as she crouched in the seat beside Brody. He patted her arm as he got out of the jeep. Harper joined him. Both men had guns in their hands and they moved into the path of the approaching car.

Vic saw them. He slammed on the brakes and stopped the car.

As the two men came towards him, Vic heard a woman sobbing with dry, rasping gasps that chilled him.

CHAPTER ELEVEN

CHITA leaned against the wall and watched the horror in Moe's face and the fear in her brother's face. The two men stood by the window, peering out into the darkness. The moonlight fell directly on them and their expressions excited her. So this was big-time, she thought. When the cards were on the table and they were all aces, then you found out who were the men, and who were the boys. Neither of these two, she decided, added up to men.

Moe said hoarsely, "Who's that out there . . . the body?"

"Who do you think?" Riff snarled. "The yellow-skin! I had to kill him! Now you've stuck your flat foot right into it. You've knocked off a Fed!"

Moe moved from the window. He was sweating and shaking.

"I didn't mean to do it," he said in a stifled voice. "The gun went off. I didn't mean to kill him."

"Tell that to the judge," Chita said softly.

"Shut up!" Riff snarled, glaring at her. "I'll get around to you! If there's one Fed out there, there'll be others. This caper's turned sour!"

Chita giggled.

"Oh, boy! Have you said something!"

Moe walked unsteadily out of the room, across the lobby and into Carrie's room.

Carrie had pulled down the blind. She had struggled into slacks and shirt and she was now standing by Junior's cot, white-faced, her eyes abnormally big as she faced Moe.

He came in and shut the door. He still held the gun in his hand and Carrie looked at it, flinching.

"Don't be scared," Moe said and he put the gun out of sight. "We're in trouble. Are you listening?"

Carrie made an effort and pulled herself together.

"Yes . . . I'm listening."

"There was a Federal Officer outside," Moe said, words spilling out of his mouth in his anxiety to explain. "I shot him. I didn't mean to. I saw something move and the gun went off. I've never ever shot anyone. I don't expect you to believe me, but it's the truth. Now, we're in trouble." He paused and looked at the sleeping child. "That means you and the bambino are in trouble too. Not from me . . . I want you to know this. I'm going to do what I can to see you right, but the trouble will come from the other two. I want to know something. It's important. Are you still on my side?"

Carrie stared at the frightened man.

"Yes," she said. "Yes, I'm still on your side."

Moe drew in a deep breath.

"I haven't much longer to live," he said. "I know that, but while I can, I'll see you right. You stay here and do what I say. I'll get you out of this if I can."

He went out of the room, shutting the door.

In the living-room, he found Riff still at the window. Chita was perched on the arm of a chair, smoking.

Riff swung around as Moe came in.

"What the hell are we going to do?" he demanded. The quavering fear in his voice made Chita giggle. "How do we get out of here?"

"We'll get the car and we'll make a break for it," Moe said, knowing such a move would be fatal. All he now wanted was a quick finish. If he could drive into a hail of bullets that would kill him instantly, he would be happy. He couldn't bear the thought of being dragged back to jail. He wanted a quick end and he wanted the baby to be safe. "We'll go the back way."

"What are you trying to do?" Chita asked, staring at him. "Commit suicide?"

"I'm telling you: it's our only way out," Moe lied urgently. "We'll surprise them. Come on: let's get out of here before they surround the place."

Frightened and sweating, Riff started towards the door. Chita slid off the arm of the chair and got in his way.

"Riff!"

The note in her voice brought him to an abrupt stop.

"Use your head!" she went on. "If we go out there, they'll blast us to bits!"

Riff hesitated.

"Don't listen to her," Moe said feverishly. "Come on . . . let's get out of here!"

Riff snarled at him. He was staring at Chita who had that glint in her eyes that Riff knew so well.

"Don't listen to this fat Wop," she said. "When we go, Riff, we'll take the Dermott woman with us. With her in the car, there won't be any shooting. They won't dare stop us so long as we have her with us."

Riff gaped at her, then he suddenly relaxed and grinned.

"Kiddo, you're stuffed with brains! Go get her! Come on! What are we waiting for?"

As he started towards the door, Moe said, "Hold it!" He had his gun in his hand and the sight pointed at Riff. "You leave her be! We'll go and we'll take our chance, but we don't take Mrs. Dermott!"

Behind the sand dunes, out of sight of the house, Vic, Harper and Brody were talking.

"Look, Mr. Dermott," Harper was saying tensely, "this is a tight spot. They now know we are out here. We can't get near the house without getting shot. They've already killed one of our boys. We're going to get Miss Van Wylie away and then we'll get more men up here to help. There's nothing we can do for the moment but wait."

Vic was nearly out of his mind with anxiety.

"My wife and baby are in the house," he said, trying to control his voice. "Do you imagine I'm going to stay here while they are up there with those killers? I'm going up there right now and you'd better not try to stop me! I have the ransom. I'm going to give it to them and then they'll quit. I don't give a damn if they get away, but I'm going to make sure my wife is safe!"

"I understand how you feel, Mr. Dermott," Harper said, "but they know we're out here. If you give them the money, they'll use your wife and baby as a shield to get away. They'll put them in their car and they'll make a break for it, knowing we won't shoot. Then when they imagine they are clear, they will turn your wife loose. They may even kill her. You mustn't go up there and you mustn't give them the ransom."

Brody who had gone back to the jeep now came running up.

"Dennison is on the radio. He wants you," he said to Harper.

Harper spun around and ran to the radio set. Brody went after him, leaving Vic on his own. Vic hesitated for a brief moment, then he slid into the Cadillac and headed fast towards the ranch house. As he swept past the jeep, Brody shouted at him, but he kept on.

Quickly, Harper told Dennison what was happening.

"And now Dermott's gone up to the house. I warned him to keep clear, but he's gone," he concluded.

Dennison swore softly.

"You've certainly fouled this one up," he said. "Get Miss Van Wylie away. Can she drive the jeep?"

Brody shook his head and shrugged when Harper asked him.

"Brody says no. She's hysterical."

"Then tell Brody to take her direct to her father. That's the first move. These three are certain to use Mrs. Dermott as a hostage . . . that's a bet. You stay where you are. If they break out with Mrs. Dermott, I want to know. If they break out without her, I'll have the road blocks set up. Keep in touch with me and don't go near the house. I want to know what's going on," and Dennison went off the air.

In the house, Riff and Chita stared at Moe as he threatened them with his gun.

"You gone nuts?" Riff snarled. "We take her with us and we're in the clear!"

"For how long?" Moe said wearily. "We're not going to add to our troubles. We're going without her!"

"We take her with us or we don't go!" Chita said shrilly.

"You do what I tell you!" Moe's face hardened. "I'm sick of you two! I've nothing to lose now. You do what I say or I'll wipe the pair of you out!"

It was at this moment that Vic's car headlights flashed across the curtain. Moe swung around and started towards the window. Chita threw herself at him, sending him reeling. She snatched at the gun and got it. She backed away as Moe recovered his balance. She pointed the gun at him.

"From now on," she said viciously, "we'll handle this."

Riff was at the window, peering through the curtains. Chita snapped off the lights. Riff recognized Vic's Cadillac. He saw Vic get out of the car.

"It's Dermott!"

"Watch it!" Chita said sharply. "Don't show yourself!"

"Gimme the gun!"

Chita handed him the gun. Riff again peered out of the window. Vic was standing motionless, looking towards the ranch house. He saw Riff at the window.

"I'm alone," Vic called. "I have the ransom."

"Palsy, you'd better be alone," Riff said. "I have a gun on you. Come on in, with the dough."

Vic lifted the two suitcases from the car and walked up the veranda steps.

"Let him in," Riff said to Chita. He remained, watching at the window as Chita went into the lobby.

Moe stood motionless, but his eyes peered around the moonlit room for a weapon. Near him, on an occasional table stood a small bronze statuette of a naked girl. He edged towards it until he was close to the table.

Aware that he had moved, Riff looked swiftly at him. "Don't start anything you can't finish, Fatso," he said.

"I'm not starting anything," Moe said. "This is the end of the road. We're not going to get away with it."

"Shut your mouth! You may not, but we will!"

Vic came in, followed by Chita who sat once again on the arm of the lounging chair.

"So we have Feds out there, palsy?" Riff said viciously. "Was this your bright idea?"

"There were two of them," Vic said. "One of them is dead. The other is taking the Van Wylie girl home."

Through the open window they could hear the jeep start up. A few moments later they saw the headlights of the jeep lighting up the dirt road as the jeep headed fast towards Pitt City.

"Yeah?" Riff sneered. "You expect me to believe that? Come on . . . how many more of them are out there?"

"I've told you. There's no one now, but there will be. In another hour the place will be swarming with them. Here's the money . . . take it and get out!"

Riff jerked the curtains into place.

"Put the light on."

Chita reached out from where she was sitting and snapped on the lights.

"Where's Kramer?" Riff demanded, glaring at Vic. "Why isn't he here?"

"Why should he be?" Vic returned. "This is your share of the ransom. He's already on the run."

Riff looked at the suitcases.

"How much?"

"Over a million and a half," Vic said.

"You're lying!"

"See for yourself."

Vic put the suitcases on the settee and snapped back the locks. He opened the cases and stood away. The Cranes stiffened at the sight of all the money packed in the suitcases. Then Riff, hypnotized by the sight of so much wealth, lowered his gun and went across to the suitcases. He had to pass Moe and this was Moe's chance. Moe's hand dropped on the bronze statuette, lifted it and smashed the base of it down on Riff's wrist. His movements were so fast the eye couldn't follow them.

The gun dropped from Riff's hand and he yelled out with pain, clutching his wrist and staggering away. Moe scooped up the gun and covered both the Cranes.

Chita hadn't moved. She sat on the arm of the lounging chair, her face expressionless, her eyes glittering.

Moe said, "Tell me the truth, Mr. Dermott. Are there Feds out there? We'll need help. I'm turning these two in . . . I'm turning myself in. If they're out there, call them in."

"There's one out there," Vic said.

"Okay, then call him in," Moe said.

Nursing his wrist and cursing, Riff leaned against the

wall as Vic started towards the door. Moe swung around and covered Riff with his gun. His back was half turned to Chita. He didn't see her slide her hand under the cushion of the chair. Her fingers groped for and found Vic's automatic which she had taken from Riff's trousers pocket the previous night and had hidden under the cushion.

Vic stepped out into the lobby. As he walked towards the front door, Carrie came out of the bedroom.

"Oh, Vic!" she exclaimed joyfully. "I thought I heard your voice."

He went to her, catching her in his arms.

"It's all right, darling," he said. "Just a moment . . . I'm getting the Federal Officer. I . . ."

The violent bang of gunfire that exploded from the lounge turned them into frozen, frightened statues.

Under the cushion, Chita had thumbed back the safety catch, lifted the gun from its hiding place, levelled it at Moe's back and squeezed the trigger.

Moe felt the impact of the bullet without pain. It was as if someone had hit him with a heavily padded sledge hammer. He went down, knocking over an occasional table, his gun sliding out of his hand and coming to rest at Riff's feet. Her face set in a white, hard mask, Chita stared at Moe, watched him as he moved in a feeble endeavour to get to his feet, then raising the sight of the gun slightly and aiming at his head, she again squeezed the trigger.

In the brief seconds before the second bullet smashed into Moe's skull, he thought of his mother. He wondered if she had been frightened to die. He regretted not being with her when she had passed on. In these brief seconds, he realized, even if he hadn't listened to Kramer, with her death, he would have had no future. People, he thought, had to live with people, and he had never had anyone to live with except his mother. With her gone out of his life, he knew he was lost. There was no pain. He knew he was dying. At least, he thought, he would never again be caged up in the awful cell. Just before the second bullet killed him he thought of the Dermott's baby.

Riff picked up Moe's gun with his left hand.

"The son-of-a-bitch's broken my wrist," he whined.

"Oh, shut up!" Chita snapped and going to the door, she covered Vic and Carrie as they stood motionless, staring at her. "Come on in," she said, "and be careful how you come."

The sound of the two shots came clearly to Harper. He immediately contacted Dennison on the two-way radio.

"There's shooting going on up there," he reported. "Looks like the Dermotts want help. Permission for me to see what's happening."

"You stay right where you are," Dennison said firmly. "In less than an hour, you'll have help. Pitt City police are sending men out to you. I must know if these hoods make a break out and if they use the Dermotts as shields. You stay right where you are and report to me . . . understand?"

"But they could be killing those two up there," Harper protested. "I can't stand by . . ."

"You heard me!" Dennison barked. "Stay where you are . . . that's an order!"

At the sight of Moe's dead body, Carrie stifled a scream, turned and hid her face against Vic's shoulder.

Riff seemed stunned that Moe was dead. He stared at his sister, stared at the gun in her hand, but although bewildered, he had sudden confidence that if anyone could get him out of this spot she could.

"Take the money!" she said to him. "Put it in the car!"

"I can't carry them," Riff snarled. "My wrist's broken!"

"Do what I say!" Chita screamed at him. "To hell with your wrist! Take the money to the car!"

Cursing, Riff shoved the gun into his hip pocket, shut the lids of the suitcases, grabbed the handles in his left hand and staggered out of the room with them.

Chita eyed Vic and Carrie. The gun in her hand pointed directly at them.

"I killed him," she said, nodding to Moe's body. "I've got nothing to lose now." She was speaking directly at Vic. "We're leaving, but we're taking your wife with us. Start something and I'll fix you and your baby! Now . . . get away from her and stand against the wall!"

"You're not taking her with you!" Vic said, white-faced, but determined, "Oh no!"

"Get out of the way!" Chita screamed at him. "I won't tell you again!"

Carrie broke free of Vic's hold.

"I'm going with them," she said breathlessly. "Vic, please . . ."

"No!" Vic exclaimed. "I'll go! What's it matter who goes?" He went on to Chita. "My wife has the baby to look after."

Riff came in silently. He was behind Vic. Chita nodded her head. Vic had no warning. Carrie suddenly saw Riff, but before she could scream a warning, Riff clubbed Vic at the back of his head with the butt of his gun. Vic went down on hands and knees, then sprawled forward, unconscious. Carrie started towards him, but Riff grabbed her.

"Let's go!" Chita said urgently. "Come on . . . come on . . . let's get out of here!"

As Carrie was still struggling, Riff hit her across her face. Dazed, Carrie's knees buckled. Chita and Riff caught hold of her and rushed her out of the house to the Cadillac. Chita slid under the driving wheel while Riff shoved Carrie into the back seat. He got in beside her.

Chita started the engine and headed the car towards the drive.

"Think they'll shoot?" Riff asked, a quaver in his voice.

"Why ask me?" Chita said impatiently. "You'll know fast enough."

Riff dragged Carrie on to his lap. He cowered down behind her, using her body as a shield. He stared with scared eyes over Carrie's shoulder at his sister who sat bolt upright, her hands gripping the driving wheel as she raced the car down the long drive towards the five-barred gate.

Dennison was poring over a large-scale map of the district surrounding Wastelands when Harper came through on the two-way radio.

"They broke out just this minute," Harper reported. "I could only see two women, but maybe the men were lying on the floor. One woman was driving, the other was on the back seat. They're using Dermott's Cadillac. They turned left at the gate: that means they are making for Boston Creek."

Dennison looked quickly at the map spread out on his desk.

"Okay, Tom: go up there, and find out what's happened to Dermott. Watch it! They may have left someone there, but I doubt it. Call back fast. I'll be waiting."

Harper picked up the two-way radio, slung it by its strap over his shoulder, then gun in hand, he ran towards the ranch house.

He arrived as Vic came unsteadily to the front door.

"They've taken my wife!" Vic said, leaning against the doorway. "You've got to do something! They've taken my wife!"

On his way to the ranch house, Harper had passed Di-Long's body. He had paused long enough to identify the body and now he started past Vic to enter the house, but Vic grabbed his arm.

"Which way did they go?"

"Towards Boston Creek," Harper told him. "What's been going on here?"

"See for yourself," Vic said. "There's a man in there . . . dead."

Harper went into the sitting-room. He found Moe on the floor. He turned him over with his foot, made sure he was dead, then he switched on the radio.

By now Dennison had alerted all police patrols within fifty miles of Boston Creek to look out for the Cadillac. One of his men was alerting all service stations to report if Dermott's Cadillac stopped for gas, adding the warning that on no account should there be any attempt to stop the car. Yet another of Dennison's men was alerting the various airports in the surrounding district.

When Dennison heard Harper's report, his face turned grim.

"They can't go on driving forever," he said finally. "Sooner or later they'll have to go to ground. So long as Mrs. Dermott is with them we can't try to stop them. Come on back, Tom, and bring Mr. Dermott with you. Tell him we are doing everything possible for his wife's safety."

As Harper listened to what Dennison was saying, he became aware of the sound of a car starting up.

"Hold it, Chief," he said, and putting down the mike, he went quickly to the window. He was in time to see Vic drive Moe's Lincoln out of the garage, swing the car on to the drive and then at a speed that made Harper gape, roar down towards the exit.

Swearing, Harper ran back to the mike.

"Dermott's taken off!" he reported. "He's probably got some crazy idea he can overtake the Cadillac." He paused as a new sound came to him: the persistent crying of a baby. "Oh, for Pete's sake! Now the Dermott's baby is yelling. What am I to do?"

"You're getting married," Dennison said unfeelingly. "You'll have babies of your own. This will be good practice for you. You'd better bring the kid to headquarters," and he went off the air.

With the speedometer needle showing eighty-five miles an hour, the Cadillac fled down the dirt road towards Boston Creek. Chita was hunched over the wheel, watching the road as it raced towards her in the powerful beams of the car's headlights. She felt exhilarated and recklessly excited. Already, she was working out a plan of escape. They had a million and a half dollars in cash! With that kind of money and with two guns, there was nothing they couldn't do, she told herself.

Carrie sat in the corner of the back seat. She was desperately frightened. Sooner or later, this mad drive would end, then what would happen to her? She thought of Vic. Had he been badly hurt? She thought too of Junior. Who would look after him?

Muttering to himself, Riff examined his swollen wrist. Very cautiously and wincing, he flexed his hand and realized with relief the bone wasn't broken, but it hurt him. Satisfied now he wasn't crippled and he wasn't going to be shot at, he began to recover his nerve. He leaned forward and shouted at Chita, "Where do you think you're going? Don't drive so goddam fast! You'll have us over!"

Even as he spoke the car lurched dangerously as Chita took a bend in the road, righted itself as she wrestled with the wheel and then she once again increased speed.

"Hear me!" Riff bawled, scared. "You'll have us over!"

"Oh, shut up!" Chita said viciously, but she slowed as they came off the dirt road on to the highway leading to Boston Creek.

"Where do you think we're going?" Riff asked again.

"There must be an airport around here," Chita said. "Our one chance is to get to Mexico. If we can charter a plane and get over the border, we'll be in the clear."

The hard coil of fear that had paralysed Riff's mind began to dissolve.

"Baby, you're stuffed with brains," he said admiringly. "Yeah, we can beat the rap that way."

"Look for a road map," Chita snapped. "Do I have to do everything?"

"Take it easy," Riff said and climbed over the back seat to the front seat. He hurriedly pawed through the pockets of the car, but he found no map. He began cursing again. Then he turned around and glared at Carrie.

"Where's the nearest airport?"

Carrie, who had been listening to their conversation and who knew where the various airports in the district were, was determined to give them no help.

"I don't know," she said.

Riff snarled at her. He leaned over the seat, doubling his fist.

"I said where's the nearest airport! Don't feed me that don't know crap! You want some loose teeth?"

Carrie stared at him, her face white, her eyes defiant.

"I don't know."

Riff hesitated, then swung around to look at Chita.

"So what do we do?"

"We'll find one," Chita said. She had noticed that the gas gauge showed the tank was nearly empty. "We're running dry. Get back to her. We'll have to stop at the next service station. Have your gun ready."

Riff scrambled over the seat and sat close to Carrie.

"Listen, baby," he warned, "I want quiet from you. If you start trouble, it'll be the last trouble you'll ever start." He now had Moe's gun in his hand.

Carrie edged away from him.

As they approached Boston Creek, they saw the bright lights of a service station. Its flashing sign spelt out C-a-l-t-e-x.

"This could be trouble," Chita said softly. "Watch it, Riff. Hit her if you have to." She put her gun under her thigh where she could get at it quickly, then she swung the car into the service station's entrance.

A big, pleasant-faced attendant came trotting out as the Cadillac drew up.

"Fill her up and skip the manicure," Chita said curtly. "We're in a hurry."

"Who isn't?" the attendant said, grinning. He poked the nozzle of the hose into the Cadillac's gas intake. "Oil, water, tyres okay?"

"Yes," Chita said.

Riff, still watching Carrie, had opened one of the suitcases and slid out a hundred-dollar-bill. Carrie sat motionless, aware of the gun that Riff was pressing against her side.

"Just as well you don't want to use the telephone," the attendant said chattily. "Been out of order all day. It's driven me nuts. Everyone, but you, passing through, seems to want to call someone."

"Well, we don't," Chita said. "Hurry it up, buster. We're in a hurry." Then she leaned out of the car window. "Is there an air taxi station anywhere around here?"

"Why, sure," the attendant said, "a couple of miles up the highway, then take the first to your left. It's signposted. It's a small outfit, run by a couple of young guys who only set up in business this year. They don't get much of the trade. They're too close to the Oro Grande airport, but you're more likely to get a plane there if you're in a hurry than if you went on to Oro Grande."

He removed the hose and took the hundred-dollar bill from Riff.

"You got nothing smaller?"

"No," Riff said.

There was a little delay while the attendant got change. The three sat silent, waiting.

Neither Chita nor Riff realized their luck that the service station's telephone was out of order. It was the only station within fifty miles of Boston Creek that the Federal Agents hadn't been able to contact.

Out of sight of the service station, Chita sent the Cadillac hurtling forward along the highway.

By now Riff was relaxed and his mind was beginning to work. This idea of Chita's to escape to Mexico had seemed pretty smart, but now, as he lolled back and watched Carrie, he suddenly saw it wasn't all that of a hot idea.

"Baby," he said, leaning forward so he could speak softly to Chita, "don't you need a passport or something to get into Mexico? Suppose these Spicks don't take us?"

"They'll take us," Chita said. "We have a million and a half dollars in cash and two guns. So they'll take us."

"Yeah." Riff flexed his aching wrist. "How's about this girl? What do we do about her?"

"What do you think? We take her with us until we're sure we are out of trouble."

Riff blew out his cheeks. He was nervous and unsure of himself.

"Think we're going to get away with this, baby?"

"I don't know, but I do know we're going to try," Chita said in a flat, cold voice.

Ahead of her, in the headlights of the car, she saw a cheaply painted sign that read: *Boswick Air Taxi Service. Two Miles.*

She swung the car off the highway and drove up an uneven dirt road that eventually led to the airport.

CHAPTER TWELVE

Vic knew the Cadillac was nearly out of gas when he had returned to Wastelands. He knew, before the Cranes reached Boston Creek, they would have to stop to refuel. They had a ten-minute start on him. Providing he drove fast enough and providing there was a little delay when they refilled the tank, he had a good chance of catching up with them. He had no idea what he was going to do when he did catch up with them, but all he could think of right at this moment was to be with Carrie.

He had made his decision when Harper had told him the Cadillac was heading towards Boston Creek. When Harper had entered the ranch house, Vic had run to the garage. He found Moe's Lincoln: the key in the ignition lock. As he switched on, he saw with relief that the gas tank was half full.

He drove as he had never driven before. There was plenty of power under the Lincoln's hood and the car shot down the long drive at well over ninety miles an hour. The gate stood open. Vic slammed on the brakes. The tyres screeched as he swung the car out on to the dirt road, then he shoved the gas pedal once again to the floorboards.

It seemed only seconds before his headlights picked out the main road. Again he slowed. He daren't risk a smash. But once on the main road, he settled down to hurtle the Lincoln towards Boston Creek at its maximum speed. Three times he flashed past approaching cars who hooted at him: the drivers shocked at his speed. The speedometer needle was steady at one hundred and two miles an hour, the maximum he could get from the roaring engine.

Hunched over the wheel, his heart pounding, Vic regretted refusing Dennison's offer of a gun. When he finally caught up with the Cadillac what was he to do? Both the Cranes had guns. How was he to get Carrie away from them?

He overtook a car that, at the speed he was travelling,

seemed to be standing still. Again he heard the indignant blast of a horn as the driver, shaken, made his protest.

Vic kept on. Minutes later, he saw a flashing sign that was spelling out the word C-a-l-t-e-x: the first service station on the road. It would be here, if he had any luck, that the Cadillac had had to stop for gas. He slowed, swung the car into the circular drive and brought the car to a screeching stop.

A big man in the Caltex uniform came hurrying out of the office. Vic got out of the car.

"Brother!" the attendant said. "You sure scared me. You going to a fire?"

"Did a blue and white Cadillac stop here for gas about ten minutes ago?" Vic asked, trying to steady his voice. "Two women and a man in the car?"

Happy to have information to give, the attendant nodded. "Why, sure. They left about five minutes ago. Friends of yours?"

Vic drew in a long breath. Friends? He thought of Carrie.

"Did they say where they were going?"

"One of them – one of the girls – asked where the nearest air taxi service was," the attendant told him. "I put them on to the Boswick airport: a couple of young guys run it . . . nice fellas . . . I thought I'd do them a good turn."

"Have you a telephone?"

The attendant raised his arms helplessly.

"It's been out of order all day. Sorry, but there it is . . . the times I've had to tell folks . . ."

"You wouldn't have a gun you could lend me?" Vic asked as he began to move back to the Lincoln.

The attendant gaped at him.

"Gun? What do you mean?"

"Never mind," Vic said and slid under the driving-wheel.

"What's this about a gun?" the attendant demanded, coming up to the car.

"Never mind," Vic snapped and sent the car roaring along the highway. He knew where the Boswick airport was. He had often passed the signpost on his way to Boston Creek.

So they were going to try to get away by air, he thought. If he could rely on the gas attendant, they were only five or at the most ten minutes ahead of him, They couldn't charter a plane and take off under an hour. He was now certain to reach the airport while they were still there.

As soon as he saw the lights of the airport, he would have to turn his headlights off. He would then have to approach slowly so they wouldn't hear the car's engine. He would have to leave the car some distance from the airport and then approach on foot. His only weapon, he reminded himself grimly, was the weapon of surprise.

Ralph Boswick a heavily-built, sandy-haired young man, replaced the telephone receiver, took his big feet off the desk and stood up.

His partner, Jeff Lancing, lolling in a discarded aircraft chair, looked at him inquiringly.

"Who was that?"

Boswick lit a cigarette, striking the match on the seat of his cavalry twill pants.

"Believe it or not. . . the F.B.I." he said and grinned. "Seems kidnappers could arrive here. A man and a woman have snatched a woman and could be heading our way. They're nuts! For the past week, no one has headed our way!"

Lancing, short, barrel-chested and dark, slightly older than Boswick, looked sharply at his partner.

"They give a description?"

"Oh, sure. The man is tall, powerfully built and dark. He's wearing a black leather outfit. The woman, blonde, is his twin sister. The other woman has reddish hair and she's pretty. They say the kidnappers are armed and dangerous."

Lancing got to his feet.

"This is just the place they might come to!" he said. "Dangerous, huh?" He went to the desk, pulled open a drawer and took from it a .45 automatic.

Boswick laughed.

"Be your age, Jeff! That iron isn't safe to fire. It hasn't been cleaned or oiled in years, and besides, we haven't any slugs for it."

Lancing hesitated, then with an embarrassed grin, he put the gun back in the drawer.

"We'd look pretty dumb if they did come here," he said.

"They won't," Boswick said. "No one comes here. Jeff . . . I hate to say this, but I've been looking at our figures. If something doesn't happen soon, we're going to be in the hole. This idea of ours isn't working out."

"The trouble with you," Lancing said, "is you're always looking for the fast buck. Everything takes time. You see, in a couple of months, we'll be in the black again."

"If we go on like this," Boswick said, taking a file from a drawer in the desk, "we'll be sold up. I mean it, Jeff. Here, take a look at these figures."

With a resigned sigh, Lancing came to the desk. Together, the two men began to go over the bills that they owed. They worked for the next hour, then Lancing tossed aside his pencil and stood up.

"I didn't realize it was this bad," he said glumly. "What are we going to do?"

"What other mugs have to do," Boswick said, shrugging. "We'll have to find another mug. We . . ." He paused as the door leading into the small office swung silently open. A girl, her hair carelessly dyed blonde, wearing a flowered cotton dress with a full skirt, her eyes very alert and watchful, stood in the doorway.

The two men stared at her.

Boswick got to his feet.

"I want a plane to take me and my friends to 'Frisco right away," Chita said. "What can you do for me?"

Lancing's face split into a happy grin.

"Why, sure. The kite's all ready. We could be on our way in less than an hour after clearing with 'Frisco. That fast enough for you?"

"What do you want to clear with 'Frisco for?" Chita asked suspiciously.

"Have to get permission to land," Lancing explained. "It won't take long."

Boswick was studying the girl. He didn't like the look of her. He suddenly remembered the warning he had had from the Federal Field Office.

He said casually, "Take the lady and her friends to the waiting-room, Jeff. Maybe they'd like coffee while they're waiting. I'll get the clearance."

"Sure," Lancing said and moved towards Chita. "This way. Won't keep you waiting long. You . . ." He stopped short as Chita lifted the gun in her hand that she had kept concealed behind the folds of her skirt.

"No telephoning," she said. "We just take off. Get away from that desk!"

Under the threat of the gun and the snap in her voice, Boswick moved over to where Lancing was standing. Lancing was gaping at Chita.

"What's all this?" he asked. "What . . . ?"

"Wrap up!" Chita said and moved further into the office. She was followed by Riff who was shoving Carrie before him. At the sight of Riff's black leather outfit, Lancing remembered the F.B.I.'s warning and realized who these three were.

Riff went over to the telephone and yanked the cable free from the wall.

"If you two jerks want to stay alive," he said as he threw the telephone receiver across the room, "you'll do what you're told! We're in a hurry! We want to get over the border and into Mexico . . . you're taking us! So let's have plenty of action!"

Boswick said, "Mexico? It can't be done. I would have to get permission to land from Tijuana. You'll run up against the passport control authorities. You just can't fly into Mexico this way."

"Yes, we can," Chita said. "You put us down in a field . . . any place. We don't have to land at any airport. We're going to Mexico and you're taking us!"

"I tell you, it can't be done," Boswick said. "You can't

put a light plane down in a field. What field? You ever been to Mexico? It can't be done!"

Riff looked uneasily at his sister.

"We're wasting time. Maybe we'd better keep moving. I never did think this idea . . ."

"Shut up!" Chita said, her voice vicious. She looked as Boswick. "We're going to Mexico! You're going to take us unless you want a hole in your belly! Get moving!"

Boswick hesitated, then shrugged.

"If that's the way you want it, then I guess that's how you'll have it," he said. "I'm not arguing with a gun, but I warn you, we could crash land! The kite's only got a short range. We could run out of fuel before we found enough flat land to park on."

"We'll worry about that when it happens," Chita said "You talk too much! Get going!"

Boswick looked over at Lancing. His left eyelid flickered.

"Better see to the kite, Jeff."

"Sure." Lancing was worried. Boswick was the dominant partner. Lancing had an uneasy idea that Boswick was planning something that could be dangerous.

Riff said to Chita, "You go with him. I'll stay here and watch these two."

"Come on, buster," Chita said to Lancing, "and don't get any bright ideas."

She followed Lancing out of the office.

Ed. Black, one of Dennison's men, dropped the telephone receiver back on its cradle.

"Every service station is now alerted, Chief," he said, "except the Caltex Station outside Boston Creek. Their telephone is on the blink."

Dennison looked up from the map he was studying.

"Get a patrol officer to call in," he said impatiently. "That's probably the one place they could have stopped at."

Black picked up the microphone. Seconds later he was in contact with a patrol car heading towards Boston Creek.

Patrol Officer Benning said he would proceed at once to the Caltex Station and report back.

Again, without knowing it, the Cranes had a lucky break. The time now was one o'clock in the morning. The Caltex attendant who had given Vic the information about the air taxi station had gone off duty and had been replaced by his sidekick who took over the shift to nine o'clock the same morning.

"I wouldn't know," he said when Benning questioned him. "I've only just come on. Fred might know something, but he's gone home."

"You got his telephone number?" Benning asked.

"Sure, but our telephone is on the blink: besides, Fred won't be home yet. He always stops off in Boston Creek some place for his dinner."

Benning got Fred's telephone number and his address then he returned to his car and alerted Dennison.

"Find him, and find him fast!" Dennison snapped.

There were a number of all-night cafes in Boston Creek, but finally Benning found the Caltex attendant just as he was leaving for home. The time now was one-forty-five. Before Benning could get all the information he needed from Fred, and by the time he had again reported to Dennison, it was a few minutes after two o'clock.

Tom Harper had arrived at headquarters, gingerly carrying the Dermott baby who had bawled without ceasing during the drive, and was still bawling, although he was being fussed over by two flustered policewomen.

"They're heading for the Boswick air taxi station," Dennison said to Harper who was looking inquiringly at him. "It's a safe bet they're going to make for Mexico. They have an hour's start on us . . . too long for us to do much, but Dermott must be right behind them. See if you can raise the airport and warn them."

Harper found the telephone number in the book, dialled, listened and hung up.

"The line's out of order."

Dennison shoved back his chair.

'I've told Benning to go up there, but to be careful. We can't close in on them so long as Mrs. Dermott's with them," he said, paused, then abruptly made up his mind. "Come on, Tom. I can't keep out of this. We'll go by helicopter." He turned to Black. "Alert Benning we're on our way and to keep in touch with us by radio. He's to get close to the airport, but he's not to take any action unless he's sure Mrs. Dermott can't get involved. Alert all patrol cars to converge on the airport but to keep out of sight. No action's to be taken until I get there."

He strode out of the office and Harper went after him.

Half-way up the dirt road leading to the airport, Vic switched off his headlights. He drove slowly, and when he reached the airport gate, he pulled up. He went around to the boot of the car, opened it and searched in the tool kit. He selected a tyre lever, the only possible weapon he could find, then moving fast, but cautiously, he made his way towards the small lighted reception hut and office over which was a flashing sign of an aircraft in flight.

He saw the Cadillac outside the office. As he reached the car, the office door opened and a man followed by a girl he immediately recognized as Chita came out. Vic ducked down behind the Cadillac. He heard Chita say, "Make with the legs, buster. You paralysed or something?"

Vic watched the two: the man ahead, Chita about three feet behind him, walk quickly towards the hangar. He waited until they were some yards away, then he moved silently to the office and cautiously peered through the window.

A heavily-built man leaned against the wall facing Riff who sat on the desk, gun in hand. Standing away from these two, big-eyed and white-faced, was Carrie.

Vic looked at her for a long moment, wrestling with the temptation to burst into the room and attack Riff, but he knew he wouldn't stand a chance so long as Riff had the gun. He moved back into the shadows, then he had a sudden idea. He went quickly to the Cadillac and looked into the back seat. On the seat were the two suitcases in which he had packed the money. He grabbed hold of them, lifted them from the car and then looked anxiously towards the hangar.

Lancing had got the hangar doors open and he, followed by Chita, was moving into the hangar. Carrying the suitcases, Vic ran around to the back of the office and into the darkness of the night.

In the hangar, Chita, standing well away, watched Lancing get the aircraft to readiness.

"Listen, buster," she said, "you're not doing this for free. It's worth a thousand bucks to you if you get us to Mexico. From the look of this crummy joint, you could use that kind of money."

"Think so?" Lancing said shortly. "How's about if I crash the kite?"

"Oh, forget it! You're insured, aren't you? Get going, buster!"

In the office, as Boswick leaned against the wall, eyeing Riff, he suddenly noticed Riff's swollen, bruised wrist. It flashed into his mind if he could get close enough to Riff and make a dive for the gun, he could get it from Riff without any opposition. With a wrist like that, the guy was practically one-armed.

"My partner can't run the kite out without help," Boswick said. "It needs two men to push it. If you're in all that of a hurry, maybe we should go over to the hangar."

Riff eyed him suspiciously.

"Why didn't you say so before?"

Boswick forced a grin.

"I guess you sort of upset me," he said.

Without looking at Riff, he walked casually to the window and looked out, Riff, alert, covered him with the gun.

"Yeah, he needs help," Boswick said, looking over his shoulder. "Let's go."

Riff hesitated, then he slid off the desk. He jerked his head at Carrie.

"Come on! You keep close to me." To Boswick he went on, "You go on ahead."

His muscles tense, Boswick walked to the office door and opened it. He was within three feet of Riff. As Carrie didn't move, Riff, snarling at her, motioned her to the door. In doing so, he half turned his back on Boswick who flung himself at Riff, his hand grabbing at the gun. As the gun was forced down, it went off: the bullet made a hole in the floor a few feet from where Carrie stood.

For a brief triumphant moment, Boswick thought he had got the gun from Riff, but he had underestimated Riff's strength and he knew nothing of Riff's years of experience of street fighting.

Unable to use his right hand, Riff stamped down on Boswick's foot with his iron-shod ski-ing boot. Boswick caught his breath in a gasp of agony and his grip relaxed. Riff drove his shoulder into Boswick's chest, sending him reeling against the wall, then snarling, he lifted the gun and shot Boswick.

Carrie hid her face in her hands and cowered against the wall. The big man stared at Riff, blood showing on his fawn-coloured shirt, then his eyes rolled back and he slid to the floor.

A few seconds before the shooting, Lancing had started the aircraft engine. Neither he nor Chita heard the two shots above the noise of the engine. Neither did Vic who had got some hundred yards from the office and had dumped the suitcases in a ditch that ran along the boundary of the airport. He then started back towards the airport as he heard the aircraft engine.

Cursing, Riff grabbed hold of Carrie and dragged her out into the darkness. He started towards the hangar, then paused.

"What's the matter with me?" he muttered savagely. "I'm flipping my lid! I nearly forgot the money!" He let go of Carrie's arm. "Wait here!" he snarled at her, then went to the Cadillac, reached into the back seat, groped for the suitcases, groped again, then alarmed, he wrenched open the car door so the roof light came on.

He stared at the empty back seat, a cold fury of rage and fear sweeping over him. He looked in the front seat. Muttering he ran around to the boot, opened it, stared at its emptiness, then slammed it shut.

The money was gone!

He was so stunned, he could only stand motionless, glaring at the Cadillac. A million and a half dollars! Gone! Who had taken it?

Watching him, her heart thumping, Carrie hesitated for a brief moment. To her right, within twenty yards from the light coming from the office window was a dense patch of darkness. If she could reach this sheltering darkness, she might have a chance to escape. She was sure these two would take her to Mexico. This was her one and only chance to get away. If she didn't take it, she couldn't imagine what would happen to her once they landed in Mexico.

Like a frightened ghost, running as she had never run before, she started towards the protective darkness.

Riff still stood like a pole-axed bull, glaring at the Cadillac. Who had taken the money? He could only think of the vanished money. Carrie was completely forgotten.

Then he came up with the answer. Chita! A double-cross! Chita!! It had been Chita who had taken his gun! It had been Chita who had dug up the yellow-skin's body! It had been Chita who had soured his chance to marry Zelda! And now Chita had grabbed the money and was taking off to Mexico and ditching him!

He looked towards the hangar, some two hundred yards from him. Floodlights suddenly came on, lighting part of the runway. Then he saw the small aircraft taxi out of the hangar. He saw Chita come out and move towards the aircraft. Under the bright lights and in her light dress, she was clearly visible not only to Riff but also to Patrol Officer Benning who had reached the airport and was now lying in rough grass, looking towards the hangar. He had seen Riff and Carrie come out of the office, but he had lost them in the darkness. Now, as he watched the aircraft, he saw Chita and wondered what his next move should be.

As he lay there, gun in hand, he heard the faint drone of an aircraft. This could be Dennison arriving by helicopter, he thought hopefully.

His mind a white flame of vicious fury, Riff lifted his gun, steadied it on the roof of the Cadillac and sighted the gun on Chita's back as she paused while Lancing manoeuvred the aircraft on to the tarmac.

In a few seconds Chita would get into the aircraft with the money and would be away, Riff thought. Slowly, his finger began to squeeze on the trigger. It was a long shot. He hesitated. Maybe he should get closer, but if he did, she might see him. She too had a gun. Even as he hesitated, he was automatically taking up the slack of the trigger. Then the gun suddenly exploded with a flash and a bang.

Vic started back towards the lighted window of the airport's office, the tyre lever clenched tightly in his hand. He had covered fifty yards or so when he came to an abrupt stop.

He saw Carrie and Riff come out of the office. He crouched down in the darkness and watched them. He saw Riff suddenly pause, speak to Carrie and then go to the car.

Vic's heart began to thump. This thug would now discover the money had gone. What would he do? He looked at Carrie who was standing motionless, outlined against the light coming from the window. He saw Riff open the car door, then he caught his breath sharply as Carrie suddenly sprang into life and began to run frantically towards him. Would Riff see her? Would he shoot after her? But no, Riff seemed to be unaware that Carrie was escaping.

Vic waited until Carrie was within twenty yards of him, then he rose to his feet.

"Carrie! It's Vic!"

Carrie shied away, stifling a scream, then stopped and looked fearfully at him. She could just make out a dark silhouette, but Vic said again, "It's me, darling."

With a choked sob, Carrie rushed to him and he caught her in his arms. She clung to him while Vic looked over her shoulder towards Riff. Relieved though he was to have her safe, he was frightened of Riff. Seeing Riff still hadn't noticed that Carrie had escaped, Vic looked beyond him to the lighted hangar where Chita was plainly visible. Then there was the choked bang of a gun that made both Carrie and Vic stiffen. Vic saw Chita give a convulsive start and then drop face down on the floodlit tarmac.

"Let's get out of here!" Vic said urgently. Supporting Carrie, pulling her along with him, he began to run towards the entrance to the airport, making a long detour to avoid the floodlit tarmac.

They hadn't gone far when a voice snapped out of the darkness: "Hold it! Stay right where you are!"

Carrie caught her breath in a shuddering gasp as Vic pulled her to a standstill. Out of the darkness, Patrol Officer Benning appeared, gun in hand.

As Chita fell to the ground, Riff experienced a sharp, agonizing pain inside his body as if a knife had sliced into him. He stood for a long, horrified moment, staring at the collapsed figure of his sister, her skirt riding up so he could see the white flesh of her thighs, the light of the brilliant lamps playing on her badly dyed hair.

The red haze of fury that had hung over his mind faded. He felt suddenly naked and alone. Then in the grip of panic, he ran frantically towards the hangar.

Sitting in the pilot's seat, Lancing watched him come. He was tempted to push open the throttle and take the aircraft into the air, but he thought of Boswick. He couldn't leave Boswick to face this hood alone. So he sat motionless, the engine of the aircraft ticking over, the propeller blade spinning, almost invisible in the bright overhead lights.

Riff reached his sister. He was panting, frightened and sweating. He bent over her. A patch of red stained her dress in the exact centre of her back. Falling on his knees beside her, he put down the gun, then very gently, he turned her over.

Chita moaned. She opened her eyes and stared up at Riff.

"Get going!" she gasped. "They're here! Make him take you ... never mind me! Get going!"

Riff wiped his face with the back of his hand.

"Where's the money?" he quavered. "Why did you take it? Why did you do this to me?"

Chita half closed her eyes. A dribble of blood ran out of the side of her mouth. She shook her head slightly, struggled to speak, then shut her eyes.

"Chita!" Riff's voice cracked. "Where's the money? What have you done with it?"

She lay silent for a few seconds, then making an effort, her eyes opened wide.

"It's in the car . . . what are you talking about? Take it and go! Riff! Don't you understand? They're here! They shot me!"

Riff sat back on his heels. Watching him from the pilot's seat, Lancing felt a chill sweep over him at Riff's expression.

He looked like a man going out of his mind.

"Didn't you take the money?" Riff yelled. "It's gone! I thought you took it! Hear me? It's gone!"

Chita moved her legs in a spasm of pain.

"Take it? Why should I take it? It's ours . . . yours and mine . . . why should I take it?"

Riff hammered the sides of his head with his clenched fists. He tore off the dirty bandage covering his ear and threw it from him. He was like an animal with a broken back: frantic with misery and pain.

"Chita . . . I thought it was you! I shot you, baby! Forgive me! I just went crazy. Baby! I'll get you out of this! We'll be all right. I'll get you to a croaker! You leave it to me!"

More blood dribbled out of Chita's mouth. She reached up and took Riff's hand in hers.

"Get going, Riff. There's nothing you can do for me. I understand . . . you get going."

"I'm not leaving you," Riff said frantically. He grabbed up the gun. "We're going together. As soon as we get to Mexico, I'll get you fixed. It's going to be all right, baby! To hell with the money! You and me . . . like always."

He reached down and scooped Chita up in his arms. She gave a low wailing cry and arched her body so he nearly dropped her. Blood ran out of her mouth and her eyes rolled back.

Riff held her close, staring at her white, lifeless face, feeling her warm blood against his chest. Then very slowly, he lowered her to the ground.

It took him several seconds to realize she was dead. Chita! Dead! He stared down at her face that had suddenly become the face of a stranger. This couldn't be Chita whom he had loved, fought with, stole with, lived with, shared everything he had owned with . . . this couldn't be Chita!

Then a wild, animal cry burst from him. The sound made Lancing grimace and look away.

Riff began to pound the ground with his fists, crying and moaning, demented in his grief.

The pilot of the helicopter pointed.

"They won't hear us with that aircraft warming up down there. I can put you down . . . they won't even see us," he said.

Dennison and Harper exchanged glances, then Dennison said, "Put her down."

Two minutes later the helicopter made a gentle landing within five hundred yards of the airport. Guns in hand, Dennison and Harper scrambled out. They could hear the busy drone of the aircraft engine. They saw the aircraft standing outside the hangar. They saw Riff kneeling beside the body of his sister, then they heard a soft whistle to their right. Peering into the darkness, they saw Patrol Officer Benning moving cautiously towards them.

"Benning, sir," he said to Dennison. "I have Mr. and Mrs. Dermott with me. There's been shooting. Permission for me to investigate?"

Beyond the patrol officer, Dennison saw Vic and Carrie. He went quickly to them.

"It's all right," he said. "This officer will take you to headquarters. There's nothing for you to worry about now. Your baby's being taken care of and is waiting for you. You get off. We'll finish this." He turned to Benning. "Take Mr. and Mrs. Dermott to headquarters right away."

Vic said, "There's a million and a half dollars in a ditch over there."

Dennison grinned.

"Never mind about the money. You two get back to headquarters. I have an idea they'll be glad to see you."

As Benning led Vic and Carrie towards his car, Dennison and Harper started cautiously towards the hangar.

Riff was now walking slowly around Chita's body. He seemed dazed and appeared not to know what he was doing. He suddenly threw up his arms and howled like a stricken animal. The sound lifted the short hairs on the back of Lancing's neck.

Dennison and Harper were close now. They covered Riff with their guns. Then Dennison raised his voice in a commanding shout: "Drop your gun and up with your hands!"

Riff spun around. He stared sightlessly into the darkness, then in sudden panic, he turned and ran. He ran blindly into the spinning aircraft propeller that sliced through his head with the precision of a butcher's cleaver slicing through meat and bone.

Crime fiction – now available in paperback from Grafton Books

Isaac Asimov
The Casebook of the Black Widowers £1.95 ☐

Colin Wilson
The Schoolgirl Murder Case £1.95 ☐

Agatha Christie
The Secret Adversary £1.95 ☐
The Murder on the Links £1.95 ☐
The Mysterious Affair at Styles £1.95 ☐
The Man in the Brown Suit £1.95 ☐
The Secret of Chimneys £1.95 ☐
Poirot Investigates £1.95 ☐

John Bowen
The McGuffin £1.95 ☐

To order direct from the publisher just tick the titles you want
and fill in the order form.

Crime fiction – now available in paperback from Grafton Books

James Hadley Chase

One Bright Summer Morning	£1.50	☐
Tiger by the Tail	£1.95	☐
Strictly for Cash	£1.50	☐
What's Better than Money?	£1.50	☐
Just the Way it Is	£1.50	☐
You're Dead Without Money	£1.50	☐
Coffin From Hong Kong	£1.95	☐
Like a Hole in the Head	£1.50	☐
There's a Hippie on the Highway	£1.50	☐
This Way for a Shroud	£1.50	☐
Just a Matter of Time	£1.50	☐
Not My Thing	£1.50	☐
Hit Them Where It Hurts	£1.95	☐

Georgette Heyer

Penhallow	£1.95	☐
Duplicate Death	£1.95	☐
Envious Casca	£1.95	☐
Death in the Stocks	£1.95	☐
Behold, Here's Poison	£1.95	☐
They Found Him Dead	£1.95	☐
The Unfinished Clue	£1.95	☐
Detection Unlimited	£1.95	☐
Why Shoot a Butler?	£1.50	☐

<u>To order direct from the publisher just tick the titles you want</u>
<u>and fill in the order form.</u>

All these books are available at your local bookshop or newsagent, or can be ordered direct from the publisher.

To order direct from the publisher just tick the titles you want and fill in the form below.

Name _____

Address _____

Send to:
Panther Cash Sales
PO Box 11, Falmouth, Cornwall TR10 9EN.

Please enclose remittance to the value of the cover price plus:

UK 45p for the first book, 20p for the second book plus 14p per copy for each additional book ordered to a maximum charge of £1.63.

BFPO and Eire 45p for the first book, 20p for the second book plus 14p per copy for the next 7 books, thereafter 8p per book.

Overseas 75p for the first book and 21p for each additional book.

Panther Books reserve the right to show new retail prices on covers, which may differ from those previously advertised in the text or elsewhere.